SOCIETY AND THE LAND

By the same author

ENGLISH HUSBANDRY

ROBERT TROW-SMITH

Society
and the Land

LONDON   The Cresset Press   MCMLIII

First published in 1953
by The Cresset Press Ltd., 11 Fitzroy Square, London, W.1.
Printed in Great Britain by
The Camelot Press Ltd., London and Southampton.

Preface

THREE ASPECTS of this book seem to call for some prefatory explanation: the theme, the method of treatment, and the subject-matter.

To save the reader time in discovering whether the theme interests him or not, I summarize it here. It is the relation which has existed and which now exists between society and the farm land and people of Britain. The past 1,500 years have been divided into four periods. First, that in which the Saxon pioneers farmed for their own subsistence; second, that in which the land became a source of dignity for the great men of the nation; third, that in which farming was followed for the profit it gave; and fourth, the present time, in which agriculture is becoming the means of national subsistence. All four periods overlap, of course; but they seem to be valid enough divisions in which to discuss the places which agriculture, the landlord, farmer and worker, and the land itself fill in the national economy. And a final chapter is added in which an analysis is attempted of the cultural significance of the land of Britain. This is, I believe, the first time that the whole of this great subject has been exclusively treated on a sustained historical basis; and for this reason alone this book will certainly contain many errors, both of interpretation and emphasis.

Second, there is the method of treatment. Historical facts are sacred; and I trust I shall be found to have treated them as such. The interpretation of these facts is necessary if a coherent and logical story is to be made out of them. But to the interpretation I have added a number of personal opinions upon the place which the land and the men upon

5

it should play in national affairs; these opinions may sometimes be ill-founded, platitudinous, tendentious, or even
foolish; but I make no apology for intruding them into what
should be an impartial historical tale because in the last
resort the proper relation between a society and its agriculture is a matter of opinion and not of fact.

Then, third, there is the subject-matter. Agriculture, and
probably agriculture of a very high order, was practised in
these islands when the Romans were here; and for long
before. But so little is known of it and it had so little influence
upon what came after that I have elected to begin with the
coming of the Saxons.

The reader will also find that the techniques and the tools
of farming are only briefly touched upon. There are two
reasons for this omission. I have already dealt with them in
more detail elsewhere.[1] And in this book I have been more
concerned with the broader conception of the place of agriculture in society rather than with the domestic details of
that agriculture.

Datchworth Green, Herts.
  November, 1952.

[1] *English Husbandry*, Robert Trow-Smith (1951).

Contents

Illustrations

CHAPTER ONE

Pioneers with Ploughs

I T IS hard today to understand the fundamental importance of the land in a primitive society. Perhaps the easiest way is to imagine oneself as one of a band of companions cast upon a desert island, with a few tools, some weapons for defence, and a determination to survive. To live, the castaways must build themselves shelter out of the materials growing naturally upon the land; feed themselves with the crops which they can grow in such clearings as they are able to make with their few inadequate tools; and domesticate to their use such indigenous stock as will give them meat and milk, motive power for their little farm, and the hide and wool with which to clothe themselves.

These castaways must join forces for the work which it is difficult or impossible to do individually; and they must evolve a rudimentary code of law to regulate the conduct of the members of their little society. Not least, they must breed strong sons and prolific daughters so that the community can survive to consolidate its first position, extend and protect its boundaries, and lay the first foundations for a far distant future when there will be release from the numbness of ceaseless toil for the few who will provide for the spiritual and artistic needs of the men and women of an embryonic nation. But for a long, long time the struggle will be one for bare survival; and without the land and its produce life at present and hope for the future must immediately cease.

It was into such a state that the Anglo-Saxons of the Dark Ages projected themselves in Britain, with an optimism that was immense and a courage that is beyond the bounds of imagination. They left a land upon the continent of Europe which they knew, under the impulse of a migration which was moving the peoples of Europe like chessmen on a board; and the chessmasters were: one an instinct akin to that which sends the migrating swallow to the south and the eel to its breeding ground in the weed of the Sargasso Sea, and the other the lust for new, empty lands to pioneer—a lust which has sent the sons of the Anglo-Saxons over the seven seas ever since. They came to an island which is today tamed and disciplined by plough and hedgerow, but which was then a waste where hornbeam and bramble fought for space beneath a thick umbrella of oak and beech and birch. Here and there in the lowland forest were the clearings where the Romanized Britons, deserted by Rome, lived within the mouldering and decaying walls of Verulamium or Viroconium. On the unforested chalk hills the descendants of the Iron Age immigrants still followed, in their rectangular fields, a primitive agriculture; and, beyond the reach of the newcoming Saxons, there were in the mountains and moors of the west and north the remnants of ancient races who tended their stock, lived upon the meat, cheese and milk which beast and sheep provided, and knew little or nothing of the arts of the plough. It was—to a brave, adventurous, reliant race—a land fuller of promise of milk and honey than that which Jehovah had offered to the children of Moses.

This was the frame and canvas of the picture. The first artists were an indomitable race seeking peace and the plough as much as plunder and the sword. The brush was the axe and spade, ploughshare, seedlip and sickle. And the paints were the grain crops that had for thousands of years been moving outwards from their origins in the Middle East, and the cattle and sheep and pigs and horses that had come from heaven knows where. How the picture was painted does not here concern us—how the ploughs and harrows were made and used, the stock bred and tended, and the harvest of grain and milk and flesh won. The whole picture of the land and the men upon it is the subject; how it has changed in 1,500 years from one of forest and field into one in which the forest has gone, the field has become a little regarded background, and the foreground is the factories and steelworks, offices and shops from which packing case and bale and metal fabrications go out to the four corners of the globe.

The Saxons can have come across the sea with few material possessions, some tools perhaps, and sometimes the foundation animals for herd or flock. But they could not leave behind them in their old homes their mental stock-in-trade of habits, customs and thoughts, evolved upon the continent and destined to shape their family, tribal and national societies in Britain. That shrewd and accurate Roman historian Tacitus has described them as he knew of them at the end of the first century A.D.: each man living in a loosely knit settlement, the community taking into cultivation one part of the wide lands which were then still at their disposal, cropping it for a year or two, and then breaking up new ground; each man receiving his dole of acres according to his rank; drinking the fermented juice of the barley grain; fearing and avoiding towns as the very graves of freedom; worshipping the hero of the battle only a little less than the gods who were themselves divine warriors; bound by ties of intense loyalty to his military and tribal chief; and all except the slaves individually free, or as free as any man can be in a cold and savage world where the community of fellowship in work and war is life, and independence and isolation are death. A brave intemperate race, valuing the keeping of faith above life itself, and the chastity of its womenfolk and the sanctity of the family only a little less; willing to work for survival, but allowing labour no inherent virtue; and eating beyond repletion when the chance offered.

In his chosen English home the Anglo-Saxon warrior-peasant installed both his family and many of his old ideas, although here and there he mated with the wives and daughters of the men he had conquered and absorbed some of their customs. The mental furnishings which concern the present argument most are the habit of communal agri-culture hinged upon family, tribal and military loyalties, the personal freedom, and the hatred of the town. The community of free peasants co-operating for certain agri-cultural purposes was the starting point of most, though not all, of the social and economic system of the English country-side, of English history itself. The co-operation probably did not extend into ownership. The arable strip, cleared from the forest or won from a Romano-Briton, was cultivated com-munally, but once it had been allocated to a settler it became that man's property, subject only to the supreme possessory rights of the tribal chief who was now becoming a local king. Of these sovereign rights more will have to be said soon, for they were the basis upon which, in the course of the centuries, peasant freedom was to decline into serfdom. It is also probable that the Anglo-Saxon settlers at first practised a run-rig system of extensive farming which had been remarked by Tacitus in Germany, in which land was broken up, used for a time until its natural fertility became exhausted, and was then abandoned for a new piece which still retained its pristine fertility. There was, at first, land enough and to spare for this wasteful agriculture; and it was only as the population expanded and filled the land that the community had to fall back upon a static, unshifting cultivation of two or three communal fields. Where the land remained thinly peopled, as in the moors of the west, the hills of Wales and Scotland and the infertile sandy heaths of the midlands and the south, that run-rig lingered on, sometimes into recent times.

Co-operation is essential in an agriculture of which the resources are limited. Today it is of benefit for the small hill farmer to join in the ownership of the more elaborate and expensive equipment, and to make good the deficiencies in internal farm labour by helping to shear his neighbour's sheep in return for help with his own. The primitive Saxon farmer found it quite essential to co-operate in the ownership of the plough and plough team, probably in harvest and the carting of the harvested crops, certainly in the shepherding of the stock, where one looker could tend the sheep or swine of many men. Co-operation ceased to be necessary only when a holding became large enough to be internally self-sufficient in labour and equipment. For most men that day was many centuries ahead; for some the strength of tradition worked for its retention long after it had ceased to be necessary. The smaller the farmer the greater the benefit which such mutual help brought; and it was when co-operation declined with the break-up of the old order in late medieval days that the little man was squeezed out of his few acres.

Community of labour meant community of interests; and in all forms of human society interests have to be protected by law from the criminal and the selfish, the thoughtless and the indolent. The earliest English legislation which survives is largely agricultural in its scope, as was to be expected, for it was not until the end of the Middle Ages that stocks and shares, urban industries, and the adventure of foreign trade began to replace the land, the domestic chattels, the farm live stock, and the farm tenantry that were the real and the whole wealth of medieval man. The whole structure of such Anglo-Saxon legislation as is known rests upon the land, its extent, its ownership, its use, and the fortunes and the misfortunes of those who lived by or upon it. Before the end of the eighth century Ine of Wessex was protecting by law the inviolacy of the common arable fields against straying beast and of the woods against trespassing swine; was providing for the public sale of stock in order to suppress illicit dealing in stolen or strayed animals; was regulating the relationship of lord and tenant; and was seeking to restrain the old tribal habits of shifting cultivation. Throughout the rest of the Anglo-Saxon period succeeding lawgivers repeated in particular the safeguards against the receiving of stolen stock. They added as time went on injunctions as to the payments from the land of the produce and cash to which the Church was becoming entitled. Throughout the 350 years between the laws of Ine and the Norman Conquest the state, either as the heptarchic kingdoms or as the consolidated England, was seeking to preserve on the one hand the life and safety of its citizens, and on the other to ensure that all men might pursue their husbandly callings in tranquillity and amity. That it often failed, in the face of internecine war, of Scandinavian invasions, of human frailty in an unpoliced state, is obvious; but the important thing is that there was in existence the recognition of a prosperous and peaceful agriculture as the very foundation of society. Without the land and its harvest mankind must perish; with the crops secured, the nation could go forward with new strength. That was a truth which primitive people living close to fundamentals could not fail to recognize.

It is no less a truth today, but too few men know it.

The basis upon which the land was settled and developed is a matter of deep uncertainty and will probably remain so. The evidence is divergent and scrappy, and it has been interpreted in almost as many different ways as there are different historians. Were the rank and file of the Saxon settlers fully free men? Was the unit of settlement tribal, military, or patriarchal? Were there nominal lords of free men from the very beginning, tribal chiefs, captains of the war bands, fathers of the hearth around which many descendants and collaterals gathered? The questions are fundamental ones in any consideration of the relationship of society and agriculture, because they are the beginnings of the tangled skein which grew more ravelled with each generation; and if the nature of the thread is unknown how can it be followed? The following answers are therefore hazarded, not in any assurance that they are the right ones, but in the belief that they are the likeliest solutions of at present insoluble problems.

The land of England was so large and was colonized by the Anglo-Saxons through so many generations that there were space and time for every type of social settlement to take place. Where a war-band pitched its last camp and, storing its swords, set to clearing and ploughing the land, there a community would naturally arise which looked to its captain as its head and his heirs as its lords. Where the tribe itself moved in mass from the Continent, then the tribal chief would continue his authority. Where the unit of settlement was the family, the head of it and his descendants would become *primi inter pares*; and as such settlements coalesced the chieftainship might be made elective. The types of the earliest place-names seem to include all these elements. The Saxon was probably a free peasant, but the seigneurial element was present in his society at a very early date, if not from the very beginning of his life in England.

Below him there was certainly the slave. The Saxon had been accustomed to look with equanimity upon the custom of slavery which he had practised in his Continental home, though he probably never reached the absolute inhumanities of the great Roman landowner; and there was no reason yet why he should change his views in his new land. The earliest Northumbrian literature tells of the servile herdsmen and the domestic women who had been captured in the border wars against the Celtic kingdoms of Strathclyde and Cumbria and enslaved; and the high proportion of farm slaves who appear in the Domesday returns from the Welsh border counties points to an enslavement there also of the Welsh tribesmen won in battle. Other evidence indicates the same condition in Devon and the south-west. Absolute slavery was doomed as an institution, however. It was uneconomic, as slave labour always is. But the greater factor in its disappearance was the opposition of the Church. The Christian ethic looked with disfavour upon the enslavement of fellow Christians, however calmly it might view the exploitation of the pagan. The ecclesiastical campaign culminated in the injunctions of the early Norman bishops against the sale of British men and women like brute beasts, and against the Bristol-Irish slave traffic. And slavery as such had gone within a century after 1066. But it is to be remarked that the displeasure of the Christian Church did not also encompass the semi-slavery of the later medieval villein; that in the twelfth century, ecclesiastical estates which changed hands sometimes included in the transfer Hodge 'with all his brood and all his chattels'; and that, by and large, the administrators of the Church estates were those who fought most bitterly against the emancipation of the serf in the closing years of the Middle Ages.

There was, therefore, the free peasant as the very backbone of society, the great working middle class of the two or three centuries which followed the coming of the Saxons. Below him—far below—was the true slave. Above, but only a little above perhaps, was the little local lord. Far above there was the king—of the tiny kingdom of Essex; of Surrey which had no existence at all in historic times; of Wessex, Mercia, or Northumbria powerful enough to wield a national suzerainty; or later of the consolidated state of England itself. The king, whatever the size and power of his monarchy, was only the top man on the ladder of a society which drew the whole of its sustenance from the land, whose prosperity was the combined prosperity of the men who tilled the soil, whose wealth lay in its crops, and whose cash resources were very small indeed. There must have been money about. There cannot have existed except in the very earliest days a beautiful 'natural' order of economy untainted by copper, silver, and gold, for very great sums of money indeed were raised from the peasantry itself for buying off the Scandinavian raiders. But the early economy was very largely a food economy, and the king literally lived upon his land. It was his in two senses. The theory of the ultimate royal ownership of every national acre certainly arose in the first days of the Saxon settlement, if in fact it was not imported ready-made across the English Channel and the North Sea. The supreme possession of every acre was vested in the sovereign—as it still is—however firmly its immediate lord sat upon it. But beyond this abstract, theoretical, all-embracing over-lordship there existed the very real royal ownership of great estates throughout the land, whose fruits were there for the regal enjoyment, as today the Sovereign or her heir is in actual possession of the duchies of Cornwall and Lancaster, their rents and their revenues.

These royal acres were to be a stabilizing force through the feudal centuries, little havens of comparative freedom in the rough sea of serfdom, for the Crown has nearly always been the best landlord in the land; but their first purpose was to feed the king in the absence of a monetary economy, the cash with which to buy his food. And it was more practicable for the king to tour his farms and feed on their produce on the spot than for that produce to be sent to his court. In consequence, the royal train progressed through the land unceasingly, and many centuries were to pass before the court became permanently stationed in one place. The effects of this relentless royal perambulation were nearly all unfortunate: for the court, which was rarely in one place for more than a few days together, left behind as many empty larders as it did bastards—if its instincts were normally directed, although very often they were not; and suitors had to chase the royal justice through the length and breadth of the land. And what the king did, the larger lords who gradually arose did in only a slightly lesser degree. From this point of view at least, a 'natural economy' had nothing to commend it. As the Anglo-Saxon monarchies became more stabilized, rents in food delivered to the royal court on its progress began to take the place of the rent eaten on the spot, and Ine at the end of the seventh century actually laid down the customary food rent which was expected from every ten hides (perhaps 1,000 to 1,200 acres): 10 vats of honey, 300 loaves, 12 ambers of Welsh ale, 30 ambers of clear ale, 2 full grown cows or 10 wether sheep, 10 geese, 20 hens, 10 cheeses, a full amber of butter, 5 salmon, 20 lb. of fodder and 100 eels. The list has a stereotyped air about it, and it is unlikely that every group of estates could provide the salmon or the eels; but it is an indication of the heavy burden which the seigneurie was beginning to place upon the peasant's acres.

The king and his followers were one materially unproductive group which was fed by the sweat of the man at the plough-handle. Another was the Church. It may be argued that many of its members did more than earn their keep—the men who brought the first elements of civilization to a primitive nation, Bede writing good history in his cell at Jarrow, the illustrators of Lindisfarne, the builders of

Brixworth, the clerks who introduced order into the chaos of the royal administration. But as the ecclesiastical domination of society, from the top to the bottom, grew so did the share which the church took of the national resources, and judgement upon the value which it gave in return must be a personal one, an individual assessment of the comparative value of Salisbury spire or the Luttrell psalter on the one hand, and the ageless miseries of Aelfric's ploughman and his descendants, who made them possible, on the other.

The impact of the great ecclesiastical vested interest which grew up in the centuries between the advent of Augustine and the Norman Conquest fell upon the land in two ways: in the immediate contribution of the peasant towards the maintenance of the parish priests, and in the rents in cash and kind which the men upon the monastic and episcopal estates paid to the monks and bishops who owned them. As churches sprang up in every village it became necessary to make some more stable arrangement for the maintenance of the services than the voluntary offerings of the local peasantry. The lord's contribution was the endowment of the parish priest with glebe land, a step which made the parson a full partner in the village agriculture. No one grudged the cleric what he could grow here, for he worked hard enough for his crop. But the voluntary gifts towards his upkeep which were gradually transformed into obligatory payments were a source of irritation to those who had to make them for 1,000 years and more. Tithe, which sprang from the Christian charity of the peasant and which could at first be given to what ecclesiastical purpose he chose, slowly became a legally enforceable payment to the tithe-owner, who, so Ethelred decreed, should receive 'the tithe of young live stock at Pentecost and of the fruits of the earth at the Feast of All Saints'. So did the plough alms which grew excessively from a penny for every team yoked to the plough to the 10 rams, 400 loaves, 40 dishes, 134 hens, and

260 eggs which the men of Warmington had to render yearly to the Abbot of Peterborough. So did light scot, under which wax or cash were exacted for the lights before the altar. So did Peter's Pence, the penny from each household for the pope at Rome. Soul scot remained a voluntary payment at death, and was therefore given more freely and more cheerfully for many centuries, except where it turned into a mortuary payment under which the Church was by custom entitled to seize a man's second best beast when he died. By and large, the Church took a heavy toll from the peasant, a toll indeed which helped to keep him in an economic servitude whence he might otherwise have found an earlier escape.

This toll of tithe and churchscot, plough alms and Peter's Pence was universal. The wealth of the land began to flow into the coffers of the church in another way when the Saxon kings and thegns fell into the habit of rewarding bishop or abbot for his services or ensuring the salvation of their own souls by the gift of estates. So widespread became this alienation of estates into ecclesiastical hands that when the Domesday Inquest was taken in 1086 the church was found to own a quarter of the land of England. It was impossible for the lords spiritual, their convents and their chapters to be peripatetic as the king was, and therefore their receipt of rents in cash or kind arose at an early date, and no less onerously than upon the royal and other seigneurial estates. Lands were generally grouped and the supply of a given quantity of food for a given period imposed upon each group. One such collection of estates, for instance, supplied for the sustenance of the monks of Ramsey for a fortnight 12 quarters of wheat, 50 measures of barley for ale and 24 for fodder, 125 hens, 2,200 eggs, 2,000 loaves, 25 measures of malt, 14 lambs, 14 geese, 1,000 herrings, and lard, beans, cheese, bacon, honey, and a considerable sum in cash. These food rents persisted for many centuries, and in 1586 some tenants of the successors of Tavistock Abbey were still paying their dues in grain. The monk was no easy master, but as yet he was content to take the utmost that an unimproved estate could provide for his comfort; the time had not yet come when he blossomed out as an improving landlord.

But although the Church drew so rapaciously into its grasp the bodies of the simple Saxon men and the land which their ancestors had worked so hard to clear and till, it may be suspected that the mental allegiance to Christianity and its servants was less complete. A thread of paganism continued to run through the fabric of rural Saxon society for many centuries. While the peasant might render lip-service to the new god whom his king had recognized, his heart still worshipped the old Teuton gods who stood so much more clearly for his primitive ideals: Tew, the great war god of the German peoples; Woden, the mighty ancestor of so many of the royal houses of Early England; Thunor, the thunderer; Frig, who multiplied men's crops in bed and in the field. The heathen festivities lie only thinly concealed beneath the Christian calendar: the feast of Frig is revived as the harvest festival, and an immeasurably ancient John Barleycorn is commemorated in a new guise upon Whitsunday. The imagery of many of the old heathenities is still with us, and in the countryside the mark of the pagan remains in many customs.

The ideals of the early Saxons in England, indeed, were still those of the Teuton fighting man, or at least as far as they were expressed in their literature. The new Englishman lived far too close to the soil to see romance in it. His hero was the fighting man, because he himself had largely ceased to be a warrior, or the martyrs of the Christian Church who caught his imagination as they did that of the American Negro and the African black man more than 1,000 years later. It is noteworthy that the idealization of the countryside did not appear in English literature until the time arrived when men could look in upon the farm and the field from the outside, from city window or monastic cell or court garden, to perceive its pleasantness and ignore its grimmer realities. Holes can be picked in any generalization, of course, but by and large the true countryman has sought outside rurality for the less intimate elements of his culture; and the townsman has been the perennial rural romanticist.

But if the Saxon did not impress his workaday domestic self on the pages of his literature, he left its indelible impression upon the almost clean pages of the open book of the English countryside. He hewed and cleared and burnt, ploughed and sowed; chose the places for his houses, and wore the paths between home and field and market town; and hedged his little enclosures from the waste. The pattern that he drew is about the most permanent thing in England. The village stands today in ninety-nine cases out of a hundred where it stood at the time of Domesday, and for no one knows how many centuries before that. Here and there it has changed out of all recognition where a great town has developed out of it; has grown into a large market town, but is still recognizable for what it was; or, occasionally, has disappeared under the green turf, one of the lost villages which are now being found again. But the village streets and lanes still largely follow the lines drawn by the early Saxon; the latest of a succession of churches stands where the first stood; and the village itself has rarely moved from where it was first planted. This same permanence has existed in the people as well as in the places probably more often than we suspect. The countryman is a comparatively immobile creature; and the odds are low that some villager today carries in his veins the blood of a Saxon pioneer of his place, or even that there is a Mus' Hobden of the line of old Hobdenius, the Romano-Briton of the day. This timeless quality of lowland England, its villages and people, its field names and its lanes, is one of the most remarkable facts in the nation's history.

The character of permanence is pre-eminently the mark of the lowland arable village with the oldest farmhouses and cottages crowding into the nucleus of the parochial atom, and the protons and neutrons of hamlets, farms, meadows, waste, and woods encircling it. It was a pattern into which each succeeding generation fitted much as its predecessor had done. By the side of this unchanging scene where man and his works seem almost as old as the face of the land itself (as, indeed, geologically, they are), the men and the settlements of the hills were fleeting and unstable elements in British history, dwarfed in time, size and achievement by the ancient mountains. The uplands of Wales have always been the wide homes of pastoral man as he has followed his flocks from the hills in summer down into the valleys in winter; where he has planted his house alone among the mountains; and where, with easily replaceable dwelling and possessions which walked upon four feet with him into the safety of the mountains, he was able to live in poverty-stricken independence while his fellows in the lowlands were ignobly subjected to feudal lords. The voice of freedom was, in many ways, the voice of the mountains. Welsh upland agriculture was hardly agriculture at all in the exact sense of the word. The prince was a great rancher, his men ranched on a lesser scale; and all broke up a handful of acres for their few poor crops, tilled them while their stock grazed in the hills around, and abandoned this temporary arable when they and their flocks and herds moved on to new pastures. It was all not very different from the first glimmerings of farming among the ancient nomads of the Middle East. The strain of independence which this centuries-long nomadic life bred in the Welshman has been a lasting factor in his make-up.

As the Saxon settlement drew towards its completion, but while land was still there for the pioneering, the picture of rural Britain may have had some resemblance to that which has been quickly sketched in this chapter. Men were still largely free, apart from an unknown number of slaves. And apart from those who served a god or king in person they relied entirely for their existence upon what they could make the land of Britain grow for them. The land was life, and if it failed the men who tended it starved to death. To crop failure through drought or rain, to the death or sickness of flocks and herds, to the ailments of men themselves which stopped their work in the fields, to the depredations of Danes from the east or of the Britons from the western hills, there could be only one end. The land made a ceaseless call upon men, and if they did not answer the call there could again be only one end—death. Later ages have idealized this primitive, essential way of life. There was much in it that was admirable, but much that no man would willingly wish himself: the discipline of hard work, but also the dulling of the edge of mind and feeling through incessant toil; the supreme satisfaction of winning, breaking, and cropping new land, but the misery and tragedy when the land failed; and the beautiful simplicity of a life in which a man made what he needed with his own hands from the material that lay around him, and here there is perhaps no 'but'. Life was a great adventure, to be undertaken not from choice, but from necessity; but to the pioneer of the sixth or seventh century Fate must have seemed hard and ugly. For every man the only security was that which he could make for himself, or that which came from his partnership in the communal work in the fields. The choice was simple and unequivocal: to plough or to perish, to dig or to die. Only nostalgia can find the romance in that.

CHAPTER TWO

Knightly Dignity
and Monkish Profit

SAXON SOCIETY saw the land primarily and almost exclusively as the source of its food. The structure of the community was still simple enough for the essential relationship between the soil of the peasant's acres and the loaf of bread upon his table to be apparent to all. And this primary purpose of the land continued to be comprehended by the people as a whole until the imports of foreign grain and meat grew, in the nineteenth century, to a level at which the Briton became nearly independent of the agriculture of his own island. But beside this pre-eminent role of the land as the sole source of men's sustenance there began to appear at a very early date a new aspect of the soil of England. As soon as man began to move out of his barbaric isolation and the groups of solitary settlers consolidated into communities the land became a commodity. By it men could be rewarded

27

for their services to the state; by it their worth was computed and their place in society was principally assessed; and on its ownership an intricate superstructure of civilian duties, military obligations and seigneurial rights of justice and local administration was erected. It was the capital asset of medieval man, to be manipulated upon a flourishing market except where the state intervened to maintain the feudal structure.

The stock and share into which men put their savings were the livestock and ploughshare that turned the soil of England from idle wealth into actively used capital. Land, *per se*, is a dormant, potential asset in all except a society that lives by the chase. It must be put to work to profitable purposes, be cultivated, cropped, and stocked in order to pay a dividend to the shareholders. In early Saxon days England was an agglomeration of a multitude of minute one-man businesses, of family and tribal concerns. As Saxon society developed and the distinction between rich and poor became accentuated —as it always does when a community grows larger and more civilized—the shareholder in the land and the man immediately responsible for its cultivation became less and less synonymous. The Norman Conquest and the reorganization of the upper ranks of society which followed upon it gave the *coup de grâce* to such old ideas of free men farming England in free community as may have existed. The shadowy suzerainty of the Saxon kings over the ownership of all the acres of England became an active, jealous, and very real seigneurie of the Norman kings and their great men over the whole countryside. Some few men persisted on their free holdings right through the centuries of feudalism, but they were of small consequence beside the gradual revolution which turned the Saxon peasant into a Norman serf and moved the control of the agrarian destinies of England out of many thousand small hands into a few hundred baronial ones.

The process was justified, quite unconsciously perhaps, by

the evolution of the much admired and, indeed, wholly admirable medieval ethic of a functional society. The community was one great brotherhood, every member of which had his purpose, within his class—to pray, to fight, to plough, or to serve the state. A man's acres were given to him for this purpose: and he was protected from exploitation by the dogmas of just price and fair shares; by the injunctions against usury and monopoly; and by the fatherly eye of an omnipotent, universal Church which oversaw international affairs, royal conduct, the ethics of trade, and the everyday activities of the common man. The theory was magnificent and valid, for the economic self-interest of the individual and the good of society rarely march together. The practice was very far from perfect. But it was something that there should be such a moral basis of society, to however base a level the activities of the society itself often descended. As Professor Tawney has written, 'The golden age of peasant prosperity . . . is a romantic myth. . . . The very essence of feudal property was exploitation in its most naked and shameless form.' The struggles of the servile peasant to rise out of his bondage were in themselves a sufficient indictment of the medieval system in practice. Until recently there has never again been a theory of comparable stature behind the community. When men threw off the shackles of feudalism and villeinage, lordship and serfdom had no further need of justification; free enterprise felt in no need of an ethical salve, for it could not conceive that it had any running sores to be healed; and it is only recently, as the nation has moved again towards a neo-medieval regulation of society, that it has been thought fitting that restrictions upon personal and commercial freedom should be reinforced by a moral purpose.

This is a digression, but a necessary one, upon the ideological basis of medieval English society. The material basis was the estate in land, which is the very hallmark of the later Middle Ages. The process of formation of these estates had gone on silently and gradually through the centuries which preceded the Norman Conquest. Many of them had probably come into being by the voluntary action of the peasantry itself. The smallholder of today, with only economic adversaries to face, often chases the chimera of independence into the bankruptcy court. One thousand years ago there can have been no greater illusion than that of the liberty of a free peasant in an age when justice was neither readily obtained nor easily enforced; when there were no reserves in cash or kind if crops failed or men fell ill, or the royal demands for Danegeld were oppressive; and when the sudden onslaught of a foreign marauder or of an unruly English thegn might wipe out home and crop and stock. The process of seeking the protection of a local magnate, of 'commendation', was the peasant's contemporary insurance against such misfortunes; and the slight services and rents that had to be given in return for a strong right arm were not onerous obligations. Piers Plowman described the process:

> All my life will labour for love of thee
> If thou wilt keep my church and me
> From the waster and the wicked that would destroy us.

The lord also initiated a system of labour services when he planted settlers upon his waste, supplied them with implements and seed and stock, and took a few days' work upon his farms from them in return. There was also the old seigneurial element by which the free peasant had made an acknowledgement of the original overlordship of king or chief or captain by the payment of food rents and by running errands when the great man was in the neighbourhood. But light obligations can grow into heavy ones where strength and power lie entirely in one party to a bargain.

How far the Saxon peasant had descended into serfdom by these processes by 1066 it is impossible to say. But it is certain that the advent of William and his band of adventurers pushed the little free farmer's head under the surface of the water for the third time; and by 1086, when the Domesday Inquest was taken, feudal reorganization of rural society was well on its way to completion. One further component of this new semi-servile order of society must not be overlooked, the ex-slave. Particularly in the west there had been much slavery in Old English times, and in Devon in 1086 there were thousands of men and their families who had no rights even in their own bodies, but who were sold in the market place at a price roughly eight times that of a plough ox. Thereafter the crusades of the Church against slavery, and sheer economics, brought about a partial emancipation—partial, that is, in the degree to which the slave rose towards liberty. The lord cast off the heavy burden of slave maintenance by giving his men houses and land in return for obligations of service upon his estate, and thereby brought more of his acres under cultivation. The ex-slave thus became another element in the preponderant class of serfs, and probably because he had risen a little way into freedom, he dragged the former freeholder some way further down into servility by making his own somewhat improved status a common denominator for all men who were not free.

In the year and books of Domesday the land of England stands revealed no longer as the home of the independent farmer-settler that it once was, but as a gigantic pawn in the seigneurial manœuvres for power. Freemen remained in some numbers, but their acres were now small. For the rest, the several thousand estates of the Saxon thegns, many of them already containing a number of formerly separate peasant holdings, had been compressed into less than 200 major lordships. And of the whole land of England, the king and his family had complete control of a little less than a quarter, the Church had more than a quarter, 170 Norman barons had nearly half, and the remaining small fraction, about one-twelfth, belonged to the royal servants, to the

handful of trusted Englishmen who had been left in possession
of their estates, and to the relics of the free peasantry.

The primary, immediate obligation of the land in the eyes
of William and his successors was to maintain the military
forces of the kingdom. The estate was regarded by the royal
eye as much for its capacity to provide a quota of professional
fighting men to his army as for any other reason; and baron
or abbot or bishop was assessed on a basis of the number of
fully equipped and mounted knights which he could
contribute to the royal force. At first the lord, ecclesiastical
as well as lay, kept these men around his person when they
were not performing their term of military duties in the field
or in the castle guard. But money was scarce, land relatively
plentiful; the knight was as anxious as any other man to
become a landed gentleman; and the idle knight around the
court or hall was a constant source of trouble. The process of
endowing the knight with land for his maintenance in
return for his military services became universal; the knight
assumed the ownership of one or more manors; and in course
of time the military service became commuted for a cash
payment of scutage. The knightly class was now free to
evolve into the minor squirearchy upon which so much of the
local administration of the counties began to fall. By the end
of the thirteenth century the tenure of land by knight service
had ceased to provide either soldiers or much of their pay.
Almost nothing is heard of scutage after 1385, and this payment was formally abolished at the Restoration of 1660; but
vestiges persisted which could be traced back to the old
military tenure of land. Even at the beginning of the
eighteenth century the Berkshire manors of Tubney and
Wytham, fields at Pusey and elsewhere, the village of
Uffington and a farm at Bagshot were contributing a few
shillings in ward money, a relic of the ancient obligations
of the abbots of Abingdon to furnish a knights' guard at
Windsor Castle. All these ancient military tenures are now

forgotten; but a very great part of the land of England is still owned by the heirs by blood or purchase of the men who were planted upon it to make a medieval army. This knight service was the fundamental feudal tenure by which men entered into practical ownership of a medieval manor, with its gamut of the profits of justice from the local courts, the tolls of the markets, and the services of the tenantry for the working of the demesne farm.

In this way the land supplied the military requirements of the State. It also provided the political, social, and economic needs of the nation by the tenures of sergeantry, which remain unrepealed, but which in almost all cases have fallen so long into disuse that their origins are forgotten and the tenures are confirmed as of fee simple by the Property Acts. Many of these sergeantry tenures are fantastic to the modern mind, but they must once have served a purpose or ungenerous kings would not have wasted so many acres upon their foundation. The manor of Kingston Russell in Dorset, for instance, was held by the service of counting the king's chessmen in the royal chamber on Christmas Day and replacing them in the box when the king had finished his game. The tenant of Stanton Harcourt looked after the menagerie of Henry I in Woodstock Park; he of Bletchingdon gave the king a dinner of roast pork when he hunted in Wychwood. The de la Mares held wide estates in return for their services *per serganteriam custodiendi meretrices sequentes curiam domine regis* —of looking after the horde of whores which followed the royal court. But beside these curious obligations, however, tenures by grand and petty sergeantry supplied the daily, reasonable needs of the State in the fields of national administration: where today the offices of State are filled by men rewarded in cash, the medieval statesman and civil servant on both national and county levels received recompense in land.

As the Middle Ages drew to their close and new economic

ideas evolved, however, a basis of cash rent, or tenure by socage, replaced the tenure by service. By the fourteenth century, when money was more plentiful and trade had expanded, cash became by much the easiest commodity to handle; and in every sphere of life it took the place of the old land tenures by personal service. The knight commuted his military service for a scutage payment; the tenant by sergeantry paid in cash; and the peasant ceased to work several days a week upon his lord's private acres and paid him a penny or two a day in lieu thereof. The gain in the ease of administration and in efficiency was immense, for it was always difficult first to compel knight or peasant to present himself upon the field of battle or tillage; and once he was there service unwillingly performed was usually service ill done. There may have been some intangible loss in the change to a cash nexus right down the ladder of society: it is impossible to assess the value of the individual bond which existed between lord and tenant. It is unlikely to have been as Utopian as the picture seen through the nostalgic spectacles of time by the seventeenth-century Humberstone, who believed that this social intimacy had 'knytt suche a knott of colaterall amytie betwene the lordes and the tenants that the lorde tendered his tenaunt as his childe, and the tenaunts again loved and obeyed the lord as naturallye as the childe the father'. The same sentimentality exists today over the social harmonies of the Victorian countryside, in which the squire and the high farmer are seen as the fathers of their people and all the inhumanity and exploitation are ignored.

Before the final, and in some ways the most important, form of tenure of the land of England is reviewed, the lay lord should be given some measure of justice. Many of his class ground the faces of the poor; others, probably fewer, treated their tenants as their sons—even as there are good and bad masters today. But considered impersonally, the lord of land often did good service to the nation by his policy of bringing the waste land into cultivation. Admittedly, he rarely sent the plough into the virgin soil for love of England or the well-being of his tenants, but rather to add to his wealth and to fortify his dignity. But none the less England is partly the wide garden that it is today by reason of the work of the landowners of medieval days. In 1092 the Anglo-Saxon Chronicle recorded that King William sent to the region around Carlisle, which had lain waste and desolate since its devastation by the Danes, 'very many country folk with their wives and their cattle to dwell there and cultivate the land'; and in Yorkshire and the Welsh Marches lords settled groups of hospites upon new land, or upon land which had been won and lost again, in order that it might be brought into agriculture. This seigneurial encouragement of reclamation went on quietly all over the country, side by side with the work of the peasant himself in clearing forests and scrub, in fencing the newly cleared land, and in adding the enclosed fields to his holdings among the common strips.

Never, in these centuries between the Saxon conquest and the close of the Middle Ages, 1,000 years, did the State lose sight of the truth that the foundation of national prosperity, the solid rock upon which England was built, was the peasant at the plough-handle—except perhaps during the full flowering of feudalism in early Norman days, when the way of life of the fighting man was valued above all else. Alongside the realization of the supreme virtue of the husbandman ran an appreciation, and a very proper one, of the part which the lord, as the intermediary between the State and the ploughman, played in developing the wealth of England, which all lay in its fields. Because the lord held the land not ultimately for his own good but so that he might be supported in the performance of his obligations—for there were no rights without duties in medieval theory—his power of sale was closely hedged about. Not until the functional basis of land ownership had far decayed were tenants-in-chief of the

35

Crown permitted to alienate their estates by sale, or to interfere with the normal succession to them of their heirs. The same restriction reached right to the bottom of the social scale: the villein occupant of the village holding could not dispose of his land or his widow marry without the consent of his lord, because the obligations of service which were tied to the holding must not be upset or placed in jeopardy.

Where, in this welter of large lords and small, of noble whore-keepers and enfeoffed knights, did the peasant fit? He had, as he has always had, his two feet firmly planted on the soil, his head bowed in toil over plough and mattock and scythe—immortalized in the poignant picture of Pierce the Ploughman and his wife at work in the cold field while their babies on the headland cried all one cry and 'the silly man sighed sore, and said, Children, be thou still'. But his head was not so deeply bowed that he failed to notice the opportunities of adding new acres to his holding, of profiting from the growing urban market for his crops and stock—of feeding 'the great mouth' of London—of freeing himself from the manorial yoke in some small detail. He was unlettered, but shrewd; priest-ridden, but well aware that the Church was clothing her stones in gold and was leaving her sons naked; unwilling to fight for masters for whom he had no love, but once under arms the redoubtable bowman who brought France low; humble in the extreme in his domestic life, and passing his nights in a timber-built hovel without windows or chimney, but the stock from which archbishops and chancellors sprang. His status, both personal and tenurial, was servile. His agriculture had to be conducted within the repressive circle of communal farming, with the crops on his scattered strips in the common fields being of necessity the same as those of all his neighbours, with his stock grazing with the rest of the village flock or herd upon the disease-ridden pastures, and with half his days spent in labour upon the land of his lord.

Beside him, on the one hand, lived the landed labourer, servile like himself; on the other hand was the little freeholder, survivor of the old independent peasantry and in the thirteenth century one of a growing band which could not be accommodated within the rigid framework of the ancient open fields. The free man had probably made a little niche for himself upon a few acres reclaimed from the forest, or as a small craftsman making shoes or ploughs or ale for his fellows; for agriculture was only a part, though by far the most important part, of the occupation of the countryside. And alongside these two was an unsuspectedly large element of landless men working for a weekly wage.

All this hive of activity was externally organized upon a manorial basis, with the villein tenant a member of the agricultural and judicial entity of the lord's manor, which might be half a village or nearly half a county. But above and outside the manor, the village stood as the supreme social unit. Lords and bishops and kings might remake the feudal jigsaw of the countryside as they liked: the men and women living in the social community of the village made their own self-sufficient little world. It was a very narrow world indeed, circumscribed by the boundaries of the parish, with little news of the outside world to entertain it except when some traveller rode through with tales of the crocodiles who wept as they ate men, or of the Ethiopian maidens who charmed the elephants with their songs; or when a friar came to preach, to sell pardons, and to seduce the women. It was a tiny world in which every man was tied to the acres he tilled, and in which he ploughed and sowed and reaped the same land from his early youth until his death. But if it was a narrow world, it was a very deep one in which every tree and hedge and furrow, every nest and pond and woodland went were as familiar to a man as the contours of his own body, and in which one's neighbours provided the whole range of human relationship.

37

It is as hard to put a finger upon the exact virtues of this self-contained, self-sufficient way of life under which men lived for so long as it is to indicate the value of the social integration and communal discipline which it imposed upon the village. It is only now that these things have gone that they are esteemed—the good neighbourliness of the rural poor, the intimate understanding between man and his environment, the family roots which went deep into the past, that on however humble a scale made man feel that he belonged and gave him the supreme mental satisfaction of the occupations and amusements that he made for himself. Such a slobbery of sentimentality and imitation has been poured upon these things that they have become suspect. The caperings of the neo-rustic folk dancers, the chromatic atrocities of the folk weaver and potter, the expensively restored cottage with garages for two cars, all are insults to the culture of a past which can never be recaptured because its earthy, uncomplicated, stark foundations have gone for ever. It is far more honest to live in downright, unashamed suburbanity than this.

It must not be thought that the manorialized society which was found in Midland and southern England was typical of the country as a whole; that everywhere through the land the servile villein farmer was the typical rural figure. Far from it. In East Anglia, for instance, the Danish invaders fixed the primitive free society which they found there. They came at a time when the peasant had not begun to come under the thumb of the lord, and as warriors-turned-farmers they kept the flag of liberty flying for many centuries. They settled in compact blocks of land, and co-operative tillage and stock-keeping seem to have been far less common in this region than elsewhere. It is an intriguing question to ask what later rural England would have been like if the Danish armies had conquered and occupied the whole country, had repulsed William, and had perpetuated their egalitarian order of society with its free contractual element throughout the Middle Ages. As it was, the descendants of the Danes, when in time they were swept into the feudal net, managed to exert a high degree of bargaining power upon their Norman masters and therefore remained comparatively free.

The habit of settling upon a compact holding and not dividing the land of the settlement strip by strip among the members of the community was also brought to the North Midlands by the Northern Army of the Danes. This fact argues that by the time the Danish soldiery settled down to their ploughs, agriculture in England was passing out of the primitive stage in which co-operative work was essential, and therefore communal control and the minute divison of the common fields were desirable; and that the Danes of the north and east were sufficiently advanced in their methods and their means of husbandry to be able to work their lands individually. It also suggests the argument that their unconquered Saxon neighbours were also passing out of the necessity for communal farming by the tenth century, but that this communal farming had become a social way of life which was too strong to be broken by anything less than a resettlement of the land, although in many places the economic need for it was over.

The border counties of northern England and southern Scotland also remained for a long time outside the Norman manorial net. Here men continued to work for themselves alone, recognizing the suzerainty of the lord, if any, only by the courtesy gifts of food. Even in central England, where the normal medieval manor was found, there was a very great variety in its organization. The villein farmers of the Fenland estates, most of them Church-owned, were far—very far—from being the ague-ridden savages of popular conception and Macaulay's imagining. In the two centuries which followed the Norman Conquest they and their masters reclaimed vast areas of land from the waters, and were building churches of the calibre of Swineshead, Pinchbeck, and Quadring to bear witness to their prosperity. Where southerners were concerned in the customary control of the common fields and of the stinting of the common pastures, the peculiar terrain of the Fenlander dictated other divisions of the assets in land: the allocation of the rights of turbary, of those of fishery down to as small a share as one-eighth of a night's netting, and of the control of the inter-village grazing where the stock of many vills pastured hoof-under-hoof and of which the marks remain in the detached parts of parishes which represent the share of a medieval village in a distant grazing. This is but one example of the manner in which the agriculture of the Middle Ages still marks the face of the countryside.

Again, there were the great royal and baronial vaccaries where the herds of milch cattle ranged over wide consolidated estates to produce the milk that made the cheese that medieval man regarded as by far the most important product of the cow because it could be kept and transported and stored, while the sale of liquid milk had to be restricted to the village. And again, the ancient pastoral pursuits of Wales and the south-west and north-west persisted; and beyond the southern parts of Scotland which came under the influence of the practices of the north of England and of high monastic farming there were the mountainous lands of the Highland clansmen of whose agriculture—if any—virtually nothing is known, but which was certainly very different from the intensive husbandry of the feudal south. All these regional differences, based upon accidents of conquest and upon variations of soil, climate, elevation, and vegetation, and upon the racial and social backgrounds of the inhabitants, were profoundly to affect the pattern of life that existed in each district almost down to the present day.

The 'natural economy' under which these various agricultural communities lived has been much praised by the medievalists who see no good in the twentieth century and a Utopia in the past. If by natural economy is meant the system under which a man grows or makes everything that he eats and uses, it is arguable that this is in fact an unnatural economy, that the whole basis both of communal life and of individual existence lies in exchange of commodities and above all of ideas. The self-contained man is hedged about in his development by his own mental and physical limitations. To live in communion and commerce with his fellows is infinitely to extend the range of his thoughts and his actions, to release him from the drudgery of the tasks in the performance of which he is less adept than a neighbour, and to give him time to develop for his own profit and that of the community in which he lives his own particular arts of life. The interchange of material as well of mental commodities is the first step along the road from savagery to civilization; and it is only when a man holds society to ransom for what he has to offer that evil and injustice arise. Medieval man sought to order the affairs of the village, city, or state so that such abuse was made impossible, and he was often surprisingly successful.

Nowhere was this prohibition against the unfair advantage more rigidly applied than in the sphere of agricultural commerce, the trade in the very staff of life. The earliest, most primitive communities must have developed a rudimentary commerce as soon as they became communities, and traded in seed and stock bulls and rams. When society began to move from the rural to the urban way of life vast new openings for trade arose. This stage returned to Britain four or five centuries after the Roman cities fell, and had already gone some little way when the Normans came. The first English towns arose from many causes: naturally, as when the advantages of the situation of a village made it the focus of a district, and the successful establishment of a market transformed it into a local centre of commerce; or artificially, as in the case of the Saxon burhs founded as defensive units or of the place which was deliberately developed as a market town by its lord, as the abbots did at St. Albans or the Templars at Baldock. For many years, even centuries, these places remained largely agricultural communities with trade as a profitable sideline. Their streets were fouled by live stock passing from close and dairy to pasture, noisy with hay-carts and plough-sleds, and filled with the urban peasantry trudging with sickle or mattock towards the open fields around. The town, first a true *rus in urbe*, grew slowly out of husbandry or military encampment into commerce and manufacture. The rate of growth was variable. The Cambridge of 1086 was thoroughly agrarian, and the townsmen's grievances against the sheriff which came before the royal commissioners were that he demanded excessive service in ploughing. At the end of the thirteenth century half the men of Colchester had no occupation but that of farming; and 200 years before, at the time of Domesday, its burgesses were farming 1,297 acres in the common fields. The picture this town conveyed, said J. H. Round, was that of a landowning community with scarcely any traces of landless and exclusively trading elements. Even as late as the sixteenth century husbandry was 'the chiefest maintenance' of the people of Warwick. Londoners themselves were much harmed by the Tudor enclosures around the city. A little earlier the town bull was an intrinsic part of the economic life of Coventry. But against these must be set the prosperous East Anglian towns of Ipswich with only 40 acres for its 538 burgesses in 1086, and Norwich with 1,320 burgesses, but only 180 acres of land among them.

The partial interest of the country towns of Britain in the agriculture of the countryside around them still survives. Upon the prosperity of farming depends the size of the bank balance of the ironmongers of Ludlow or the auctioneers of

Banbury. Time has not driven the wedge between the two very far. But the schism between the farm and the industrial town is complete. In the Middle Ages, however, the towns of Britain were almost wholly dependent for their food upon the land of Britain—almost, but not quite, for when the home crops failed grain was brought in, from Ireland, for example, at the end of the eleventh century or from Germany in the middle of the thirteenth. But, by and large, the island fed itself completely until Tudor times, when imports of grain became somewhat more frequent, and almost completely until little more than a century ago. There were, in fact, even some surpluses for export, and it is likely that shipping space and the lack of any marketing organization were the limiting factors in developing an export trade in grains. Even so, England was at the time of the Norman Conquest sending some cheese to Flanders and some grain, beer, cheese, and hides to Scandinavia, in addition to its slowly growing shipments of wool.

The growth of towns, with their non-productive mouths to be fed, of castle garrisons for whose provisions the sheriff had to enter into large contracts, the increasing demands of the royal court, and the armies that were almost always campaigning in France or Ireland, Wales or Scotland, all meant that the markets for farm produce expanded rapidly in the two or three centuries after the Norman Conquest. The Irish campaign of 1171, for example, was provisioned by 3,000 loads of corn; 2,217 bacon pigs were sent to Rouen in 1203 for the armies in Normandy. And it has been computed that by the middle of the fourteenth century London had a population of 35,000, of which certainly half grew none of its own food. The opportunities for agricultural expansion were immense, and all classes of society in the countryside were quick to seize upon them, according to their capabilities. Among the villein peasantry and the ranks of the little freeholders there arose a land hunger, no longer for acres with which to feed themselves, but for acres to crop for cash. The old simplicity of the villein holdings, more apparent from the regimentation of the Domesday records than it was perhaps real, was on the way out; and in its place there was coming in that phenomenon of English society, the yeoman farmer rising from servility into an affluence and independence that had their contemporary parallel nowhere else in the Old World. The seigneurial class split: the one section, handicapped by lack of capital, desire, or ambition, leased its land and retired to found a new class of rural *rentiers*; the other part, with both foresight and funds, amassed lands in its own hands and exploited them for the wealth they could now bring. All these new moves upon the rural chequer-board fall within the compass of the next chapter, in which they will be seen as a principal part of the disintegration of medieval society. But of all the opportunists the greatest by far was the Church—for the simple reasons that it was the best organized and the most highly educated—and its emergence in the vanguard of rural development belongs to the Middle Ages as they moved towards the peak of prosperity.

Since its establishment from Rome by Augustine and from the west by the missions of the Celtic priests, the Church in England grew through the centuries into a control of the whole mental outlook of medieval man which remained unbroken until the time of Wyclif. It worked, of course, more through the lingering sub-conscious superstitions of paganism and a vague good feeling towards mankind than through the intellect; although the scholars built upon the superstitious basis an incredibly complex superstructure of logistical argument. There was for long almost no revolt against the ethical and mental superiority of the Church, although many ill words were directed against its officers. This supremacy was achieved and maintained because the Church was then an active, militant agent which dominated the community, and which did not hesitate to bring thrones low by its weapon of excommunication. It also won its supremacy because, however much it preyed upon the superstitions of simple minds, its personal example followed closely the humility, poverty, and sincerity of its founder. It began to lose its power as its behaviour changed from that of the saintly, ascetic Cuthbert to that of the worldly monks seeking wealth through office and the land first, and God a poor second. It lost its power completely as its conduct became so scandalous and its hold upon the public affection so weak that Henry VIII transformed with little internal protest a Church that had been a branch of a universal omnipotence into a department of state. It would be an exaggeration to lay the blame for the whole of the decay of the Church in England at the door of its wealth in land; but it may be suggested that the golden fleece and golden grain that flowed into the monastic granges were principal factors in the decline of the moral fibre of the Church, and its final undoing. But against the debit of the spiritual abdication that reached its peak in later centuries there must be put to the credit side of the Church's account with the world its great example as the first significant rural improver in Britain.

Pious kings, pious nobles, and the pious poor liberally endowed the Church with land from the earliest days of its foundation here; and the older monasteries had, in the century before the Norman Conquest, augmented gifts by wide and prudent purchase of estates until religion was based upon a very sound material foundation indeed. The Church, intent upon its spiritual and administrative functions, was at first content to take such rents in cash and kind as issued from its estates; and these estates had been principally bestowed upon the monasteries that began as simple, humble centres of spiritual contemplation and missionary endeavour that appealed to the puritanism that was latent in the English character. As one of the fathers of the Cistercian order wrote,

45

*in civitatibus, castellis, villis, nulla nostra construenda sunt cenobia,
sed in locis a conversatione hominum semotis.* But, as on the one
hand urban and other markets were opened for farm produce,
and on the other hand the first fine fervour of monasticism
died away, the monk found himself with vast estates at his com-
mand and immensely profitable ways of selling the crops which
could be grown upon them. The combination inevitably led
to the high monastic farming of the twelfth and thirteenth
centuries and of the early fourteenth century, and with it to
the development of a great ecclesiastical vested interest in
the land. The Church found itself committed in its own
interest to the maintenance of the *status quo* of feudal society
in the countryside. Its economic self-interest made it the most
conservative of landlords, fighting to keep the last ounce of
villein service and personal servility alive. And centuries of
vigorous estate building had made the monastic acres very
wide ones indeed: the Bishop of Ely had in 1251 more than
70,000 acres, over a quarter of which he farmed himself.

The agricultural improvements made upon their estates
by the monastic landlords can be traced in the records of the
great abbeys and priories. The picture which emerges is one
of abbots and priors who would have found the conversa-
tion of Townshend and Coke of more interest than that of the
learned fathers of the Church, and who, like Samson of Bury,
preferred the active to the contemplative life and praised
good officials more than good monks. The picture includes
the brethren of the great foundations who were competent
estate agents above all else; the beginnings of a farming
literature which was being evolved for the use of these very
estates; and monastic farms which were capital concerns,
grain and wool factories producing largely for cash. The
lands of the monastery were brought into hand, and high
farming developed and was maintained over very many
decades; for the abbey and the priory were undying communities with continuity of administration. Henry of Eastry

at Canterbury farmed with immensely businesslike methods in the collection of produce, in the careful scrutiny of market reports, in the sale of home-grown food at high prices here and the replenishment of the larder by cheap buying there, in leasing out the dairy herds. The gross revenues of the estate of Christ Church, Canterbury, in 1331 were the equivalent of more than £75,000 today. Ely Abbey put great quantities of grain on the market. Even the small house of Kingswood in Wiltshire had more than 100 labourers and thirty-five shepherds on its pay-roll in the middle of the thirteenth century. The biographer of Abbot Samson at Bury St. Edmunds wrote that 'he made many clearings and brought land into cultivation. . . . He built barns and cattle sheds, being anxious above all things to dress the land for tillage.' The monkish farmers of Tavistock conducted experiments in cereal varieties, and by high manuring 'achieved results which by contemporary standards may fairly be called brilliant'. The marshes and moors were reclaimed: in Kent by Christ Church; in the Fens by Ramsey, Ely, Crowland, and Peterborough, thus anticipating the work of Vermuyden by several centuries, and where Geoffrey of Crowland put all the considerable Peterborough profits back into works of ditching, draining and marling; in the Somerset lowlands by Glastonbury; and, greatest of all, in the remote corners of England and Wales by the vast sheep farms that surrounded the Cistercian houses.

The Cistercians, indeed, set the pastoral pattern of British agriculture for some centuries to come in the fifty and more houses which sprang up after the first had been founded at Waverley in Hampshire in 1129. They, above all, destroy the illusion of the self-sufficiency of medieval man. Under them farming ceased to be a way of life and became an industry. Ever since then the most efficient and productive farmers have pursued an industrial agriculture and, broadly speaking, the least competent in the purely material sense have been the family farmers. Against the merits of high production to feed the growing number of hungry mouths, however, has to be set the social wisdom of maintaining a close link between the bulk of the people and the soil. From this time, the closing centuries of the Middle Ages, this link began to loosen rapidly. In the fourteenth and fifteenth centuries there came the greatest of all turning-points in the history of Britain. Before, the men of these islands had ploughed and reaped and bred stock to feed and clothe themselves. Afterwards, agriculture and animal husbandry became an industry, albeit the greatest by far of all the nation's industries. This generalization must be qualified at every point, of course. There was some industrial farming before the grand climacteric; and there has been very much agriculture for self-subsistence since, as there still is. The change was partly in practice and in the pattern of land use; but, far more important than either of these, it involved a shift in the mental outlook, first of the individual and then of the nation, of quite fundamental importance in the social and economic history of Britain.

CHAPTER THREE

Shepherds be Ill Archers

IN A primitive society which has advanced far enough along the path to civilization to discard hunting and plunder as the sole sources of its sustenance, agriculture and livestock husbandry become the chief means by which the members of that society fill their bellies. The peaceful man must plough or tend his animals if he was to eat; if he neglected these tasks, he perished. But when the production from the soil exceeded the needs of a man, of his family and of his dependants, and of the tribute to the owners of the land, a surplus arose for sale to the non-producer in the town, the Church, the army, or the government service—or occasionally to the foreigner. Commercial agriculture came into being, and as the flow of produce grew as methods of farming improved and more acres came under the plough or the domestic hoof the profit motive superseded exclusively subsistence farming in importance. The land thus progressed through three stages: first, as the source of the food of the settler who cultivated it; second, as the principal buttress of the dignity of the great man into whose hands it came; and, third, as a factory in the field, in which a highly profitable industry might be pursued. Through the fifteen hundred years since the Saxon settlement was begun all three stages have overlapped: there is still some farming for self-subsistence, pride of acres has not wholly given place to the other vanities, and the commercial agriculture which reigns supreme had its origins in a period which long preceded the Norman Conquest. But by and large, the agrarian course has run through these three stages in succession; and parenthetically, may now have entered upon a fourth: farming for national subsistence.

The drama of change, from subsistence farming acted against a backcloth of seigneurial dignity based upon land ownership to industrial farming for profit, began in earnest in the closing centuries of the medieval period—say in the thirteenth to fifteenth centuries. By the sixteenth century it had assumed proportions which were alarming to the old ideas. But before this process is considered in some detail one point must be made: if the proposition is accepted that it was necessary for the future happiness and well-being of the people of Britain that the nation should move out of an almost purely peasant economy into an industrial, imperial, and thickly populated economy, then the commercial development of farming was an absolutely essential component of the process. It is not the wholly evil thing that some would have it to be. Its by-products have often been deplorable, as rural eviction, tyranny, and class hatred were, but its results have been magnificent in their perfection of technique and craftsmanship in the field and in the byre. This achievement of perfection has needed the elbow room of wide acres and the leisure, broad outlook and financial stability of a moneyed gentry and yeomanry in which to be developed. It would have been reached with far more difficulty by a nation of smallholders. Whether it has been worth the degradations of pauperdom, the futilities of an urban civilization and the divorce of the mass of the people from the realities of daily relationship with the land is another matter altogether, and will not be argued here.

There were four prerequisites of an industrial agriculture, four guide-posts which had to be erected to indicate the road to profit from the soil. They were the evolution of a technique of land use on a large scale; a sufficient market for the cash crops produced; the capital to finance it; and a radical change in the economic philosophy of the governors of the nation.

The way to large farming was lighted by the example of the Church. Some mention has already been made of its achievement here, but it is probably in the field of pastoral husbandry that its work had the greatest influence on future centuries. The cynic might even say that it was a better shepherd of sheep than of human souls. Of the ecclesiastical bodies, the Cistercian Order took the agrarian lead when in the twelfth century it established its houses in the wildernesses of England, Scotland, and Wales, as its founder had directed. The abbots seem to have planned their farming upon ambitious lines from the very beginning. A fertile soil was chosen, such hindrances to an extensive agriculture as villages or manorial rights were swept away, and a ring-fenced estate in the best traditions of later centuries was brought into being. Upon their spacious and unencumbered acres the Cistercians directed an arable farming and a livestock husbandry that were models of efficiency for the time; and, excepting the limitations which unimproved stock and seed imposed upon them, might still rank today as agriculture of the very best sort. The Cistercian example was followed on a somewhat lesser scale by the other monastic orders, by the secular bishops, and by a few lay land-owners—Thomas of Lancaster, Henry Lacey of Lincoln, the de Fortibuses—who had the foresight to see where wealth lay and the business ability to translate their plans into practice in the field.

The Cistercians and their fellow-travellers—the Benedictines were not far behind in their arable farming—cast their eyes around for promising lines to pursue in their industrial agriculture, and they alighted upon that placid and rather stupid herbivore, the humble sheep. This animal was no stranger in British farming. It had been a principal buttress of the semi-pastoral economy of prehistoric man upon the chalk uplands; in Saxon days it had grazed in its thousands upon the coastal marshes of Essex and elsewhere; and it was to be found upon almost every manor, village, hamlet, lonely hill farm of the island—dropping its dung upon a starved soil, by its treading and browsing keeping the scrub at bay, and giving the milk and meat and wool that fed and clothed mankind, a compendium of all the virtues indeed, until it began to eat up men's livings. Sheep farming was, in fact, never the prerogative of the large estate, and peasant flocks were a far from negligible factor right through the Middle Ages. But it was in monastic hands that it reached its apogee.

The rise of an agrarian economy founded upon sheep husbandry was pregnant with consequence for the future: it gave to England her first big export trade and stabilized the national finances, it opened the eyes of everyone to the advantages of farming outside the restrictive circle of the medieval system, and, perhaps, it gave to a tired but resilient soil the rest it needed from centuries of overcropping with corn—but this last is a controversial point. For the late medieval farmer the sheep had many points in its favour. Its calls upon labour were low, and except at shearing time a shepherd or two could tend many hundreds of animals; it needed almost no water. It was therefore cheap farming in the matter of annual expenditure. But, and this is a point which is often ignored, it was a type of farming which called for more capital than had to be sunk in the simple arable equipment of plough, harrow, seedlip, sickle, and flail; and the risks were greater, for the whole capital could be destroyed by murrain, while the arable man lost at most a year's crop. The principal product oɪ sheep farming, the fleece, was a commodity which could be readily stored for a favourable market, and wool was easy to transport. The close sweet grasses of the chalk downs and wolds and the hills of the Welsh and Scottish borders grew a wool which was the best in the Old World, with the possible exception of the finest Merinos of Spain, where the early agricultural trade union of the Mesta organized the pastoral activities of the country with an efficiency which exceeded even that of the British monks.

The sheep spread slowly over the face of Britain, and their wool, exported to the weavers of Flanders, became of such importance in the national economy that in 1297 it was believed to account for half the wealth of the whole land. It was to the country what coal and steel and textiles combined were to Britain at the height of its industrial prosperity. But in all this the new emphasis upon livestock husbandry fitted at first into the pattern of the countryside without unbalance. It was ancillary to arable farming, and not a substitute for it. It was practised by the ecclesiastical and lay lords upon the wide open spaces of the uplands where few men had ploughed, or even lived, since prehistoric days; and by the peasant upon the waste of the manor, the rough grazings which had not yet been reclaimed and fenced. It added to the national wealth, made the great fortunes for the wool merchants and exporters which found expression in the quiet perfections of Stokesay Castle, Paycocke's at Coggeshall, and Grevil's at Chipping Camden. It caused hardship to none, and there was no complaint against it.

The last half of the fourteenth century and the first part of the fifteenth saw the recession in population and prosperity which followed the Black Death and the succeeding outbreaks of endemic plague. The first effect of the Black Death of 1349 was a shortage of labour, which was a new thing in British farming. The man who worked for wages upon the demesne of the lord was quick to take advantage of the scarcity of hands, and demanded higher pay from masters who had no alternative to employing him but that of seeing their land untilled and uncropped—unless they were fortunate enough to get the help of the Welshmen and Scotsmen who, overfilling the small labour market in their own pastoral lands, sought work in the arable fields of England. Parliaments came to the rescue with the wage-fixing legislation of 1350 and later years which sought to remedy the 'grievous discommodity' occasioned by servants in husbandry who would not work unless 'they receive excessive wages'. It was the first serious effort by government to regulate labour, but it failed all along the line because in fixing a wage which was below the normal rate their action was seen for what it was, an act of power in favour of one class as against another. It also failed because the farm hand was seeing the light of better things. More money was buying for him luxuries which had never been his before: 'Labourers before were not wont to eat of wheaten bread; their meat was of beans or coarser corn, and their drink of water alone. Cheese and milk were a feast to them, and rarely ate they of other dainties; their dress was of hodden grey.'

The small landed peasant class who were also part-time labourers for a wage were similarly becoming emancipated from their manorial indignities. Small revolts against feudal discipline were becoming frequent. And, above all, the scarcity of manpower was giving the workers a feeling of power, of indispensability, which they were never again to enjoy until the two great wars of the twentieth century put farm labour at a premium for the second time in British history.

The unrest reached its climax in the revolt of 1381, when half England was ablaze and it seemed as if the well-ordered condition of society was to go up in flames. The small peasantry who, Piers Plowman said, were waxing fat and kicking, looked back into Domesday Book and found therein none of the services they were now being required to perform upon the manor; and they listened to the Mad Priest of Kent as he preached to John Nameless and John the Miller and John Carter his doctrine that all men had been created equal, that villeinage was the work of sinful man, and that their insurrection could remove the dead hand of the Church from the face of the land and smooth out all social inequalities. Richard II, parleying at Mile End, consented that serfdom should be abolished, that all feudal services should disappear, and that all villeins should become free tenants. The poor, simple men who heard and believed him went home with his charters in their hands, to find them revoked and their last state no better than the first.

The problems of labour, of personal and tenurial servitude, were not to be solved by a month of insurrection, but had to await their slow solution by the natural working of economic change. But this economic process did not work in favour of the underdog. Population and markets declined, grain prices fell, but labour asked more for its services. The high-farming landlord was forced to draw in his horns, by farming his land as cheaply as he could or by leasing it and retiring to live in oblivion as a *rentier*. The basis of many a prosperous yeoman line was laid when a newly emancipated villein added to his 30-acre holding land which he had leased from his lord and nursed with his own family labour until better times returned.

To those who kept their land, cheap farming could mean only one thing—sheep-farming; but, of course, it was not farming, but the ranching of wide acres for the production of a raw material for the greatest industry of the day. This reversion to pastoralism is the countryman's natural reaction to an agricultural slump, then as it was in the 1870's and in the period between the two recent wars. It is the reaction of every producer whose market is hit to keep the machines turning over as inexpensively as possible, whether in factory or field. For the time being the change did no harm. The area under food crops declined, but as the mouths to be fed were not there either that did not matter. And as the years passed the flock-masters met a rising market, and by their growing wealth financed the magnificent national recovery of Tudor days. Fleeces this time did not go overseas, but into the little cloth factories, many of them set up after the dissolution of the monasteries in the old abbey and priory buildings, where the whir of the loom replaced the chanting of matins and evensong and compline, and into the cottage homes of the rural weavers. The cloths that came out were the incomparable worsteds of Norfolk, the narrow measures of Suffolk, the handy warps of Essex, the woollens of Severnside, the kerseys of Devon, the coarse cloth of Yorkshire, and the products of the Cotswolds; and the cloth went overseas to found Britain's first export trade and the fortunes of a large number of Britons. All this wealth of material which went to clothe the rich men of Europe was seized upon by the contemporary economists as the justification of sheep-farming, for in exchange for it there came into England the foreign goods which she could not make herself. Their theories have a very modern ring.

Sheep-ranching is extravagant in land. It has been estimated that in 1450 there were 8 million sheep in England and Wales. It is unlikely that the rate of stocking upon the unimproved grasses was more than two ewes and their lambs to the acre, so that there were 4 million acres under sheep, which is a considerable slice of the country. The meek, it seemed, were indeed inheriting the earth. When there were few men to be fed, these acres could be spared, for in many decades of the late fourteenth and early fifteenth centuries land was a glut upon the market in many, but not all, places. But in time the population recovered from successive plagues, and by the end of the fifteenth century a new generation of countrymen found themselves landless when they wanted land. To a breed of men to whom the field was still the natural habitat and the town an exotic and malodorous flower, this seemed a terrible thing. It is doubtful whether very much of the old tillage area had really gone under grass, but as the medieval centuries passed the strips in the open fields had become little islands of anachronism in a sea of commons out of which younger sons had hewn holdings for themselves and squatters had settled without much hindrance. In legal theory, the lord of the manor was lord of the waste, having overcome the peasants' right of user by a long process of attrition; in practice, common rights were vital elements in the economy of the village, the grass upon which held the balance between tillage and stock husbandry. And as the centuries passed and the commons dwindled in size this balance became a most precarious one.

When sheep grew more and more profitable as the home cloth industry expanded in the late fifteenth century, it became important to the flock-master to draw as much land into grass for his flock as possible. There were three ways in which he could do this: by turning his own land from tillage into pasture by consolidating his open field strips and enclosing them; by taking peasants' holdings in hand as they fell in; and by enclosure of the waste. All three courses harmed the common folk of the countryside: the conversion of dominial land into pasture reduced the openings for employment; the seizing of common holdings and the enclosure of common waste severed the links between innumerable families and their ancestral acres, largely because the peasant had no better title to his holding than that given him by custom. To be fair to the landlords, it must be said that Henry

VIII's policy of debasing the coinage had brought about such a rise in prices that men with land had to squeeze the last penny out of it; and the profit now was in wool and not in corn. But the root of the trouble lay deeper, and the peasantry had themselves partly to blame for the rural revolution. The intransigences of their forefathers after the Black Death had forced the landowners into sheep, but who could be blamed for lack of a foresight which would have had to range over a century ahead?

Not only did the golden hoof encroach upon men's acres, but also upon men's souls. In the medieval prime, land was a dignity which carried with it both rights and duties. Now, in the early Tudor days, the dignity remained (twice in the last quarter of the fifteenth century were dukes demoted for lack of acres); the rights were still there, grossly swollen; but the sense of duty of land ownership was on the way out. A new breed of landowner had come into being. Most—not all—men who prosper exceedingly do so by trampling their neighbours under foot. The Tudor *nouveau riche* had risen often enough in this way to leave his evil mark on the face of the countryside. Fortunes had come from meeting the commercial needs of the growing towns, in financing the Crown out of the profits on wool, in the cloth trade, and finally in speculation in the monastic land which the Dissolution threw upon the market, the second of the great redistributions of land of the second millennium—the first was the Norman Conquest and the later ones were still some centuries ahead. Of the hundreds of thousands of ex-monastic acres which the Crown sold or leased ridiculously cheaply, one-quarter went to the secular Church, and of the rest one-quarter to peers, one-seventh to royal officials, one-tenth to courtiers, and one-twelfth to men of commerce. Some of this land was retained by the gentry and added to the estates which were to remain the foundation of their territorial influence for 400 years. Some of it went to 'put a halo of rural gentility around the head of many an urban magnate'. The rest became a commodity for barter, a source of high profit from rack-renting, or of quick profit from re-sale.

Much of the land of England and Wales was now in the hands of financial realists who had the capital to farm it in the new ways, to whom it represented pounds, shillings, and pence; and not upon which a proud and careful husbandry of grain and stock and men could be practised. The rural habit of respect for more ultimate values than that of the money-bag descended in time upon the financiers who became farmers, of course, for the countryside eventually puts the worldly ambitions of those who deal with it into perspective. But for some decades the profit was the only thing; and the old high morality of ownership had gone for ever. True, the last few diehards still revered the creed that forbade a man to be a great taker of advantages against his neighbour, but the sermons and tracts of the idealists of the *Common Weal*—of Latimer, Hales, and their fellows—were poor and ineffective shields against the rampant new doctrine that a man might do what he would with his own. 'If the possessioners,' Crawley wrote, 'would consider themselves to be but stewards and not lords over their possessions, this oppression would soon be redressed.' The new squires were castigated in print and from the pulpit: 'never were there so many gentlemen and so little gentleness.' Medieval thought was making its last stand for the recognition of society as a spiritual organism and not as an uncontrolled— and soon uncontrollable—economic machine.

Tudor government had to go some way into surrender to the new thought; but it set its face against the most pressing contemporary manifestation of it, enclosure for pasture. It is important to appreciate the difference between this and enclosure for tillage. The throwing together of scattered lands in the common fields, and their fencing perhaps, for easier ploughing, sounder cropping, and more freedom of management increased yields and profits, improved rather than spoilt openings for rural employment, and brought a prosperity into the countryside which was reflected in the solid, well-fashioned homes of the late sixteenth-century yeomen which are found throughout England and Wales, and to which the centuries have added a charming patina of time. Enclosure for tillage was, indeed, a necessity if a growing population was to be fed from the nation's own resources; and from this time forward the pressure of population upon the national larder was the supreme economic factor. But enclosure for pasture was a different matter. Two social reasons against the diversion of land to the hoof have already been cited: rural unemployment and rural depopulation. Unemployment was now casting its shadow over the countryside for the first time in Britain's recorded history; hitherto men had been workless only when they had been too ill, too old, or too rich to work. Now they might become workless because there was no work for them to do. 'Lords devour poor men's goods in gluttony and waste and pride,' Wyclif had written of an earlier age, 'and they perish for mischief and hunger and thirst and cold, and their children also.' Edward VI was told in a sermon—and it was an age when home truths still came from the pulpit—that 'thousands in England beg now from door to door who have kept honest houses'. And More, in that oft-repeated passage from *Utopia*, wrote pathetically of the 'poore, selye, wretched soules, men, women, husbands, wives, fatherlesse children, widowes, wofull mothers with their yonge babes . . . awaye thei trudge . . . what else can they then doo but steale and then be hanged?' Rural depopulation followed the unemployment, and the unemployment succeeded the enclosures for pasture, and the pasture was needed for the sheep that had become 'so great devowerers and so wylde that they eate up and swallow downe whole fieldes, houses and cities'.

The contemporary philosophical economists were not

fully aware of the causes of the new state of society. They put the blame on the covetousness of those who earned their profits at the hurt of others rather than on the debasement of the coinage to which Henry VIII had to resort by reason of his poverty, with the resultant inflation. The complaint voiced in *The Common Weal of this Realm of England* has a very modern note, for it arose from circumstances which have a very close modern parallel: 'Where manie of my occupacion and other like heartofore died riche men, and bene able to leave honestly behinde them for theire wives and childred . . . now we are scante able to live without debt or to kepe anie servauntes.' The husbandman was luckier than the *rentier* or the merchant for he could live upon himself except for the iron for his ploughs and harrows and carts, the tar for his sheep, and shoes, caps and linen and woollen cloth for his family. The answer of enclosing and ranching land whereby there was made a mcrc solitude and utter desolation was the natural one. Again, the solution which the *Common Weal* men proffered was a modern one: 'to make the proffitt of the plow to be as good, rate for rate, as the proffitt of the graisiers and shepmasters'. It was, in other words, the manipulation of the market of the modern Keynesian thinkers. They were wise enough to realize that profit is a good carrot to lead men into the right economic paths, and the penalties of the law a poor stick with which to drive them. They suggested that the price of wool should be brought down by restricting exports, pointing out that the imports in exchange which would be lost would be commodities that might 'ether be clene spared' or else sufficiently made within the realm. If this were not done, they said, the tillage lands would fall still further and the nation would have to import corn from 'outwarde partes and paie deare for it'.

The official concern of the state, which was reflected in so much fruitless legislation, was partly that the nation should be defended. The first state attack upon sheep-farming came in 1489, with a statute in restriction of the alienation of arable land and the destruction of houses which were pulled down when several farms were run into one for sheep-ranching. A second Act in 1515 was followed by a commission of inquiry into all enclosures made since the first Act of 1489. Two more Acts followed in 1534 and 1536. Hales and the *Common Weal* men forced the appointment of another commission in 1548, which was instructed to ascertain who kept flocks of more than 2,000 sheep and who had taken common land in hand, and whether the old monastic lands were still in tillage. The government was clever enough to use this survey as a basis for assessment under the Subsidy Act of 1548—the Tudor budget—for a tax on sheep. This, as the earliest essay in the control of agricultural policy through the pocket, was an example of a device with which we are very familiar today, when cropping of the farm is directed by price-fixing and subsidy. It was, moreover, symptomatic of the profound break in the English tradition of farming. Once, when the land fed the men who cherished it, such a device would have been unnecessary. Now, with commercial farming largely released from the bonds of self-subsistence, it was a necessity.

As has been said, Tudor concern over the depopulation of the countryside arose from the view of the governors of the realm that the prosperity of all the rural classes was the foundation of national defence. The yeoman and his man were the body and stay of the kingdom, and without them it would be left open and ready to the hands of the king's enemies. There were shepherds, of course, but 'shepherds be but ill archers'; while, said Coke, 'I dare let slip a hundred of good yomen of England or Wales to five hundred of such ribaldry' as the peasants of France. This conception of the countryman as the sane, stable, and reliable element in the population of Britain survived for many centuries, and is still common. It was certainly true once when the townsman had a poor eye, weak lungs, and marched ill, and was easily swayed in the mass. It may no longer be true today.

The Tudors at any rate had no doubt about either the virtue of the rustic as a warrior or the necessity of his role in the national economy. This role has never been so decisively indicated as in the Act of 1563, the Statute of Artificers, which laid down both the universal obligation to work and the priority of callings. It was significant that agriculture headed the list, and that the crafts ancillary to farming stood second, with the merchant and the lawyer at the bottom of the scale of social usefulness. The statute was a re-enactment and a co-ordination of previous legislation, and it was also a part of the ambitious design by the state to regulate industry for what was conceived to be the common good—by the circumscription of the activities of the commercial monopolist and the protection of the wage-earner from exploitation. It was almost the last broadside which the gallant ship of benevolent autocracy fired at the new order of things; and it failed, as the efforts to restrain enclosure in its man-eating form had failed, because the execution of the orders of the central authority lay in the hands of the local rulers, who had every interest in their failure. The rural justice of the peace had by now become the local maid-of-all-work of the central government, and it was upon him that the administration of the statutes rested. The commission of the peace in every county was recruited from the second eleven sort of landowners, the new squire who was the lineal successor of the manorial lord who had lived upon his estate, and the city magnate who had bought his halo of acres. Both were the very men who were engrossing, enclosing the waste and the commons, and sheeping the face of Britain. It was not to be expected that they would present themselves before their own sessions.

This agrarian revolution which was worrying the state so deeply involved not only changes in the techniques of husbandry and of land use, but also altered the face of the countryside and the complexion of society in the village. Two or three hundred years before, when manorial farming had been at its peak in the arable counties of England, the village had been ordered upon a roughly equalitarian basis, conducted its own affairs and presented a solid front to attempted aggression by the lord of the manor. Its integrity arose from the fact that almost every man had a beneficial interest in the land. Some tilled more acres than others, of course, but there were on the one hand few landless labourers, and on the other hand there was only an occasional villager whose holding was substantially larger than those of his neighbours. That order of society persisted for perhaps three centuries after the Norman Conquest, not as an immutable state, but as one which changed so slowly as for the movement to be imperceptible to any one generation. A mere century of plague, labour shortage, falling population, inflation, and the coming of the sheep had changed that in what, to the slow-moving medieval mind, seemed the twinkling of an eye. Some of the villein virgates were put one to another as the tenants were starved out or squeezed out, or as the ambitious villager absorbed the acres of the indolent; the commons were cleared of the villagers' stock, fenced, and appropriated; the sharp practices of the new magnates who bought the old monks' land turned paternally administered estates into vehicles for getting rich quick, a use which was alien to the old rural habits of thought. But many of the small tenants, the emancipated villeins, remained upon their lands; many of the smallholding, part-time labourers kept their acres; many commons were not—and some have never been—enclosed; and much of what seemed to the peasant to be sharp practice was merely a normal rise in rents to correspond with soaring prices, which doubled or trebled in the sixteenth century. There were two sides to the picture.

There can be no doubt that the revolution in the country-side was far less widespread than either state or moralizer admitted. Society, relatively static for so long, was being shaken by what was only a small deviation from the *status quo*; and it had found a magnificent new medium for its complaints in the printing press. But the revolution was none the less real because it was only partial; it concerned not only men's material possessions, but also their ways of thought. The cleavage between the landed and the landless was becoming deeper. A new rural middle class of yeoman and small gentry which began to emerge from the manorial shell in the twelfth century was becoming fully fledged; and an old landless class, which was once comparatively in-significant, but never absent from the British scene, was now becoming larger, less cared for, and therefore more shiftless. As these two sections diverged, the schism between master and man became more marked, to the benefit of neither. The stability of the village population was also breaking up. As one reads through the court rolls of the medieval manor the strength of the link between the village and the family is abundantly evident; and it was made greater by the control which the lord exercised over the migration of his folk. The John atte Grene who was fined a penny in Datchworth in Hertfordshire in 1420 for fouling the lane with his dung-heap came of a line which can be traced back for more than two centuries, living in the same manor and probably on the same plot of ground. And the chances are that he came of the stock of the men who first settled on the green no one knows how many years before the Conquest. As the fifteenth century progressed all this is changed, and as manorial control lessened names of new families come into the rent roll and go out again rapidly like Bede's sparrows in the ill-lit hall. Stability was giving way to mobility; Hodge was moving out of his ancient rut, to find himself chased through space and time by the scythe blades upon the whirling wheels of the chariot of progress. It may be said, on the other hand, that he was being emancipated from his countless generations of servility upon the soil; that he was becoming free, for a time, to seek his fortune upon the pavements of the town, where only the mud and slops hid the golden paving. Whether he lost or gained is a matter less of fact than of opinion.

With the villager there were also departing from the face of the countryside some of the villages themselves, victims of the new commercial agriculture—and be it noted that commercial is not necessarily used in a derogatory sense. Every county in the island can show the scars of its lost hamlets, of the villages which disappeared when the sheep came, or estates were enclosed and depopulated, or rural slumps intervened, or a gentleman made his park as the ancestors of Coke did to the mortal wound of the medieval village of Holkham. The scars are now healed over with the grass of the centuries and show less to the eye than do the mouldering walls of Scottish crofts. But the green mounds in the corner of a field tell to the discerning eye the story of a steading or street or church which was deserted by man, crumbled and decayed, and became covered by the turf. Often there is no mound, but only a change in the colour of a crop to tell the tale.

Both villagers and villages were falling victims to that impersonal force which is loosely called economic necessity. In spite of the many arguments to the contrary, a peasant agriculture is static in improvement, relatively unproductive, and a completely insufficient basis upon which an adventurous, full-blooded, and surging nation can build up its commercial and imperial greatness. It was inevitable that it should gradually disappear from Britain. As medieval changed into modern times, the rate of its going quickened. In this chapter we have considered the beginning of its departure; and it may be acknowledged that with the peasant way of life there went out for many Englishmen much of the happiness of daily communion with one's own acres; much of the balance of vision, of sanity of thought, of stability of purpose which only the association of man with the land can give; and much of the profound rural morality which made each man his brother's keeper. Its loss was a grievous one, but it may have been necessary that it should go.

Harfordshire wheeld plough

CHAPTER FOUR

Merchant Adventurers in Land

HISTORIANS HAVE sought the end of the Middle Ages in many political, social, and economic manifestations, in more than one century, and in face of the truth that history is a seamless garment. It is an unprofitable pastime. The division between medieval and modern times is no easier to detect in man's relationship with the land than in any other matter. All that can be said is that in the first half of the fourteenth century the villein tenant was still rendering most of his labour dues in return for his strips in the open fields, his servility in personal and tenurial status had scarcely begun to be undermined, the Church was the greatest single factor in English farming, and the ethic of the just price which had descended from Aristotle through Aquinas was unchallenged. But when Elizabeth died and James Stuart came south from Scotland to succeed a Welsh queen upon the throne of England villeinry had gone, the yeoman farmer was cultivating in freedom a holding which often consisted entirely of enclosed fields, the Church had lost most of its land and all of its lead in agricultural thought, and the conception of land use directed by legislation to national ends was already coming under question by the first forerunners of the school of *laissez-faire*.

The schism between medievalism and modernity has most recently been detected in the move of rural influence from the early Tudor Church to the late Tudor manor house. There is more than an element of truth in this view. The sixteenth-century blossoming of the spirit of enterprise came to fruition no less in the little chronicled revolution in husbandry than in the mental adventurings of Shakespeare and the exploits of Elizabeth's beloved pirates. The agrarian revolt which first manifested itself in the shape of the sheep eventually moved into the arable field. The authors of the revolution were the men of commerce who, coming to live in the semblance of rural gentility in the manor houses, applied the principles of business to the art of husbandry. It was unquestionably the best thing that could have happened to English agriculture; although, more questionably, perhaps not the best thing that could have happened to the peasant who farmed the land before the merchant took it.

In spite of all that has been written about the way of the land as a way of life, the truth is that profitable farming is in the long run the best farming. When land is cultivated for subsistence of the men who till it, it need not be, and indeed often is not, fully farmed. But when the land is farmed for profit there must be taken from it the last ounce of food that it can economically produce consistent with the observance of such rules of good husbandry as are designed to maintain the capital fertility and which are not—as they sometimes are—merely outworn and disproved traditions. The new business-man in the old manor house still had to adhere to the old bases of husbandry, of ploughing and seed-time and harvest, of stock-mating, birth, and death, the ancient processes of John Barleycorn; but he brought a fresh and an open mind to bear upon them. He was not satisfied with the plough, which had descended little changed from the implement which the Saxons had developed from a pre-Christian prototype, with the cereal varieties which for centuries had shown little or no increase in yield; and in one sphere at least he sought to improve the ancient British livestock by imported animals. And what was being done by the gentleman farmer in the manor house, by the man of commerce to whom riches had brought a rural respectability, could be and was copied by the new yeomanry on their growing acres. The results are to be seen in the pages of agricultural literature and in the few hints of practice in the field which survive.

The first of the native English farming manuals was written in the middle of the thirteenth century by the monkish Walter of Henley and a few of his contemporaries. When three centuries later the Derbyshire Fitzherbert and Tusser the doggerel poet-farmer brought out their agricultural text-books they could show little or no advance in agrarian theory over their remote predecessors. By the middle of the seventeenth century Blith and the other practical men with pens in their hands were marking a very considerable development in agricultural thought; the clovers were coming into use to enrich the English pastures, the proper balance between arable and grass husbandry was beginning to be understood, the value of drainage was becoming appreciated, and plough design was moving towards the modern conception. This earlier revolution has been over-shadowed by the immensely more publicized work of the great farmers of the eighteenth century—Tull, Townshend, and their contemporaries—and it has gone largely unmarked by the historian. But there can be no doubt that it took place.

It arose from the new spirit of enterprise in land use which has already been noted, from the changed outlook of the landlord who saw his wealth not in the length of the nominal roll of his tenantry, but rather in the pecuniary profits from his estate. He often farmed a large part of it himself, and the rest he let at high rents which were themselves the strongest of inducements to his tenants to get the most out of every acre for which they were now paying so much. There is, indeed, no stronger inducement to high farming than a high rent; and nothing more conducive to low production than land cheaply hired. The spirit of enterprise, in so startling a contrast to the lethargy of all but a few of the medieval lords, was fathered by a broadening and deepening of education, aided by the printing press, and by the continually growing stimulus of rising markets for the produce of the land. The theories of Aristotle and the Schoolmen were no longer accepted as the only explanations of the working of the universe and all it contained. Men's inquiring minds turned to empirical experiments in every field of life, and not least in agriculture. They also looked over the English Channel and borrowed from their Dutch neighbours both ideas in plough design and, from the natural cattle pastures of the Netherlands, the animals—enshrined in the pictures of Cuyp and Ruysdael and Paulus Potter—which laid the foundations of Britain's future supremacy in dairy breeds, and from Dutch fields the new crops of turnips and clovers. Indeed, the full story of the indebtedness of British farming to the Low Countries during the seventeenth and eighteenth centuries, and perhaps earlier, has still to be written; and it may prove that much of what is best in our farming practices we owe to Dutch inspiration. British agriculture was following, along parallel lines, the development of farming in the medieval Netherlands. By the middle of the thirteenth century both Ghent and Bruges had become densely populated towns relying upon cloth-manufacture for their incomes and the countryside around for their food; and Dutch agriculture had responded by improving itself, as British agriculture was improving itself in its own similar circumstances three centuries later.

There were, indeed, some very material elements in the late sixteenth and early seventeenth century which contributed to the expansion of the area and the improvement of the method of English farming—English because both Scotland and much of Wales still lay beyond the pale of progress. First, the population. In 1500 the population of England and Wales had stood at about 3 million, or roughly double that at the time of Domesday four centuries before. In 1600 it had probably passed the 4-million mark, and by 1700 it was nearly 6 million. In other words, for every mouth to be fed from the cultivated or pastured land of the country in 1500 there were two mouths by 1700; and the mouths were not only more, but they were in the bodies of men who were more and more ceasing to be agriculturally productive themselves, and who were demanding a variety and quantity of food far greater than that with which their forefathers had been satisfied. The long march had begun towards the time when it was, apparently, to become physically impossible to feed the people of Britain from the acres of Britain. We shall be in a better position when we reach the end of the seventeenth century to estimate how well the island was providing for its inhabitants. Here there may be noted the remark of Bacon in 1592 that there was such an abundance of grain that 'whereas England was wont to be fed by other countries, it sufficeth now to feed other countries'.

One other major factor was directing the course of the new Stuart farming. Wool, after doubling in price in the middle decades of the sixteenth century, remained stationary throughout the seventeenth; but wheat, which had remained at about 6s. a quarter until the 1540's, had jumped to an average of nearly 35s. for the decade from 1593 to 1603. Wages had also risen, but by nothing like the same proportion. What the economist of today would call the labour cost element became a less important factor in agricultural production; and arable farming, with its high calls on manpower, recovered the attraction it had lost two centuries before; and sheep-farming lost its advantage. Yields of grain were also rising rapidly from the low medieval levels, when the most that could be hoped was the return of 5 bushels of wheat for every one sown; and Harrison could write at the end of the sixteenth century that 'our countrymen are grown to be more painful, skilful and careful through recompense of gain than heretofore they have been: inasmuch that my synchronic or time-fellows can reap at this present great commodity in a little room; whereas of late years a great compass hath yielded but small profit.'

Bacon shrewdly observed that the growing yields of corn and the greater financial return from them 'invited and encouraged men to break up more ground and convert it to tillage than all the penal laws for that purpose made and enacted could ever by compulsion effect'. And Blith in 1652 estimated that by then tillage was twice as profitable as grazing. Cornfield and pasture came into equilibrium, not parochially but regionally and nationally.

This new balance of land use was immensely to the benefit of the soil of Britain. The island, as has often been remarked, is naturally divided into an arable area of the east and south and a pastoral area of the west and north-west by both altitude and rainfall. To put the land to its natural and most profitable use, it was necessary that men should be released from the chains of self-subsistent agriculture under which, if bread was to be had by the Devon villager, it had to be grown precariously upon the arable plots ploughed out of the unkindly, acid, sodden soils of the border of Dartmoor. Only when markets grew up and transport by road or water became more rapid did environment assume its full power in dictating the best cropping. As the old order of things died out production for the market replaced production for home consumption, grain assumed its proper place in the national farming, and a natural land use became possible and widely followed. But it was not followed without criticism, for even as late as the end of the seventeenth century Roger North deprecated the fact that where land was not naturally fertile it was grassed down and turned to taking a 'lazy profit' from sheep. It has always been a fault of many agricultural commentators in every century to see much virtue in a field of corn, but none whatever in dog-and-stick farming.

Costs of production accordingly fell as grain became largely confined to good arable land, and the national average yields rose; and the pockets of the men who were putting the land to fuller use than ever before became well lined. From this time onwards the best of the drier soils have remained under the plough, the areas of high rainfall under grass, and the intermediate—marginal—types have been the weathercocks of the economic wind, in pasture in times of food plenty, in arable in times of war. They are the acres which, except in times of scarcity, may not pay to farm intensively.

But to return to the seventeenth century and the men who made its farming great. The vast landed estates of the end of this century had not yet become the hubs of agricultural enterprise. The spirit of adventure was manifested in the ranks of squire and yeoman, and the squire was that sort of man whose travel was seldom further than the next market town, whose talk was of the price of corn, and who, ill at ease in high society, 'must home againe, being like a Dor, that ends his flight in a dunghill'. Overbury's character was unsympathetically drawn, and indeed much contemporary thought was antagonistic to the men who could boast new riches but no old blood, but who, as justices of the peace, were members of the most influential class in England. Willis wrote, in *Times Whirligig*, of—

A spawne sprung from a dunghill birth
Now prince it in our land.

Their commercial rawness may have been much in evidence
at first, but the paternalism of the rural tradition soon
descended upon them. They were, indeed, not far off the top
of the social ladder, for when Elizabeth died in 1603 there
were only fifty-nine peers of the realm, eight of whom she
had made herself.

The old gentry who could live upon themselves, or who
brought in money from commerce or adventure overseas,
and the new merchant gentry both held what land they had,
and bought more as opportunity offered. The old gentry with
nothing but a fixed rent roll were swamped in the tide of
soaring prices, and their lands passed to the more fortunate,
the more adventurous, or the more unscrupulous. Those who
lamented the old ways noted that the new man was 'half
Farmer and half Gentleman', whose horses went to the
plough all the week and were put in the carriage on Sundays.
The older society of the countryside resented the incursion of
this class into agriculture: Kett's rebels prayed that they
might be debarred from grazing stock except for their own
larders, and a sermon of 1550 besought the congregation to
'Loke at the merchauntes of London, and ye shall se, when
as by their honest vocation and trade of merchandize God
hath endowed them with great abundance of ryches, then
can they not be content with the prosperous welth of that
occacion to satisfy themselves and to help other, but their
riches must abrode in the countery to bie fermes out of the
handes of worshipfull gentleman, honest yeoman, and pore
laboring husbandes'.

Standing side by side with the rural gentry were these same
'pore laboring husbandes' over whom so many paeans of
praise have been sounded—the yeomen of England, 'middle
people of a condition between gentlemen and cottagers or
peasants', and 'petty proprietors without scutcheons and

75

crests'. Even contemporaries showered compliments upon this class, and Overbury, whose character of the country gentleman had been so hardly drawn, became fulsome over 'the ancient yeoman of England. . . . Though he be master he saies not to his servants goe to field, but let us goe: and with his owne eye, doth both fatten his flocke and set forward all manner of husbandry. . . . He is lord paramount within himselfe, though he hold by never so meane a Tenure. He neede not feare his audit, for his Quietus is in heaven.' Sir Thomas Overbury probably knew his squire, 'that gentleman in Ore whom the next age may see refined', better than he did his yeoman. Just as the squire had sheathed his sword and taken up his Fitzherbert and his Tusser, so the yeoman farmer was ceasing to follow his plough in the old way, as it went from one tiny strip in the open field to another, and was finding profitable new ways of managing his rural enterprise by his mental rather than by his physical exertions, 'prognosticating today of corne, cattell, butter, cheese and such other, what price they will beare for a yeere or two to come'. A bellyful of hard work and a modicum of traditional lore were no longer enough in an age when communal interdependence had gone and when it was a case of each man for himself and the devil took the hindmost.

The yeoman by no means concentrated his talents upon the husbandly crafts. In the course of the rise of the purely rural industries those who followed them had always had one foot on the land. And those who farmed as their principal occupation had always dabbled in profitable sidelines: the blacksmith made the shoes for the oxen and the shares for the plough, but he also farmed his own virgate; the villein and his wife combined the cultivation of their acres with the brewing of ale for their neighbours; the butcher was often a grazier and continued to be until the wars of the twentieth century turned the slaughterman and purveyor of meat from one man into two; the miller grew some of the corn he ground; the charcoal-burner found his raw material in the woods around his land. Those ancillary occupations were domestic, pursued for moving a little of a neighbour's money from his pocket into one's own. The rise of the cloth industry brought the village worker into touch with a wider world of profit, and the yeoman produced broadcloth from the loom in his hall as well as bread corn from his fields—'wheresoever any man doth travell you shall fynde at the hall dore . . . the wiffe, theire children and theire servants spynninge or at their cardes carding.' Those who had coal upon their land mined it, and the husbandmen of the Weald of Kent smelted their iron ores with the timber from the woods which they cleared. Indeed, it was often difficult to tell who was a farming industrialist and who was an industrialist farmer, as it often is today; so much so that Coke spoke of the 'clothiers who dwell in greate fermes abrode in the countrey, havyng howses with commodities lyke unto gentylmen where as wel they make cloth and kepe husbandry and also grasse and fede shepe and cattell'. All this diversity of occupation was added to the handicrafts which all men and women in the countryside had of necessity to pursue—the arts of house-building, carpentry, brewing, preserving, baking, and making clothes and pots and pans—which stood them in such good stead when they went to make a new home for themselves in the New World. It is, perhaps, one of the great losses of mankind today that the specializing, departmentalizing trends of the three centuries since have made him helpless in all but one or two aspects of living, and have replaced a first-hand knowledge of the material arts of life with academic learning at second or third hand.

If the yeoman class can be taken to represent the average farmer of early Stuart days, then it is evident from the incomes which it was receiving that agriculture was a profitable occupation. Yeoman, of course, is a loose term, ranging from the energetic owner of wide and fertile acres on the one hand to the unenterprising small owner on the other, living in little more than a hovel and as dirty in habits as his food was coarse. Ignoring this latter extreme, the yeoman in the opening decades of the seventeenth century was making £300 to £500 a year, according to the crop yields and the state of the market, and this in terms of contemporary money values. It was significant that the greater part of those whose incomes qualified them for compulsory knighthood and who compounded out of the honour were yeomen. There were computed to be 10,000 men at this level of income, with 60,000 who were rather less affluent. The value of these incomes may be gauged from the relative prices of labour then at 4*s.* and now (1952) at £5 a week, of wheat then at 35*s.* a quarter (1593-1603 average) and 134*s.* now. The russet-coated worthy had his pockets lined with gold indeed. And even if contemporary estimates of incomes are suspect, the proofs of yeoman prosperity remain in the little plaster halls of Hertfordshire, the stout Norfolk flint homes, the cob houses of Devon growing out of the native soil, and the solid elegancies of the limestone counties that represent a comfortable, if homely, affluence; in the inventories that lie dustily in the vaults of Somerset House with their endless lists of cupboards full of pewter pieces, of four-posters and their feather beds, of fine table linens and well-equipped dairies and brewhouses; and in the word pictures of tables laden with beef and pork and mutton, capon and goose pies, venison, cheeses, and the syllabubs.

Whence came this prosperity? Certainly from English grain; less certainly from English livestock. The southern half of the island was regarded as a corn country *par excellence.* In the middle of the sixteenth century, before the agrarian revolution had got under way, the Venetian Envoy noted that 'grain abounds, and there would be much more did not the natives show fatigue, but they satisfy their wants and seek nothing more'. A century later another observer said that England was a 'famous kingdom for corn'. The new generations of farmers endured the fatigue which their fathers had shunned, for it brought them much profit. Their grain went to market—Camden noted the 'incredible' quantities of grain which were sold weekly at Warminster market—and there met a varying fortune. A good harvest or a bad made an immense difference in the price, and transport was difficult enough to mean that gluts and famines were often only regional. But the product of the corn harvest was rarely sold at a loss.

In a normal year England grew enough corn with which to feed its people, but the great range of prices—for example, from 20s. 10d. a quarter in 1592-3 to 56s. 6d. in 1596-7—would seem to indicate that the margin of safety was not yet very wide. Scarcity was still attributed to the belief that 'more ground is employed to pasture'. There was, in fact, an obsession with bread grain, an awful fear that men could only too easily starve in a new order of society in which people no longer grew their own food, but were dependent upon the whim of an independent, capitalist farmer who no longer felt that he should be his brother's keeper. The obsession was so great that there was even opposition to the introduction of such industrial crops as madder and woad for dyeing and the diversion to them of acres which should be growing the staff of life. Houghton, in the last quarter of the seventeenth century, was one of the first men to argue that 'it seems more in the national interest of England to employ its land to the breeding and feeding of cattle than to the produce of corn'.

The effect upon the poor of the violent fluctuations in grain prices needs little emphasis. And when famine was abroad men suspected that the farmers hoarded their produce against a rising market. The justices constrained the constables to draw the grain out of the barns, and the preacher took as his text the sentence from Proverbs, 'he that withholdeth corne, the people will curse him'. Public suspicion was certainly sometimes well founded. The problem of feeding one county from the granaries of another, which often brought a local famine, was in the process, but only in a slow process, of being overcome by the growing activities of the middleman, a class then still despised and rejected of men but upon whom the welfare of the nation was becoming more and more dependent. When every man was a peasant who grew his own food there was no need for any medium of distribution; but when the time came when a few men were growing food for the many the corn merchant became an essential member of society, the indispensable adjunct of an industrial agriculture and an increasingly urban population. But the old dislikes died hard, and not until 1772 were the laws against forestallers, regraters, and engrossers repealed and a fully free internal trade permitted. The growth of towns had made the concession long overdue, but only London had been powerful enough to win exemption from the repressive statutes and permission for the city's grain dealers to 'buy and pass without any stay'.

London and, in a lesser degree, the other big towns were exerting a greater influence on English—and British—agriculture as one century followed another. By 1600 London housed 200,000 people, of whom only a tiny fraction produced any part of what they ate. It was an insatiable market, not only for the half a million quarters of bread and ale grains that it consumed, but also for the meat which formed so large a part of the diet of the Englishman of the time. The city authorities themselves bought great quantities of grain when prices were low, stored it in the metropolitan granaries which they had built, and sold it to the public when prices rose against them. The policy, an early example of bulk buying by the representatives of an organized society, was one which had an incalculable but certainly large steadying influence upon markets in the counties around, and often further afield. The neighbourhood of London itself was becoming a highly productive region except upon the poorer soils of Enfield Chase and the Surrey hills. There is a charming word picture by Norden of Harrow, where 'a man may behold the fields around about so sweetly to address themselves to the sickle and scythe, with such comfortable abundance of all kind of grain that the husbandman which waiteth for the fruits of his labours cannot but clap his hands for joy to see this vale so to laugh and sing'. Hops came from Essex, fruit from Kent; the malt from Ware and Royston, made from the barleys of the eastern Chilterns, Bunyan's delectable mountains; vegetables from the encircling market gardens of Middlesex, whence 'the wyfe or twice or thrice a weeke conveyeth to London mylke, butter, cheese, apples, peares, frumentye, hens, chickens, egges, baken'; and hay and milk from Hertfordshire, with much stable manure and other organic waste of the city returning in the wagons to feed the cold clays of the county. These and other sources of fertility were at a premium, and Platt spoke of manure as a goddess with a cornucopia in her hand.

The meat trade of London in the earlier centuries is very much of an unknown quantity. A large amount of it walked on the hoof to the metropolitan slaughter houses via the suburban pastures and Smithfield market, from the pastoral counties of the north, Midlands, and west; and the great treks of the black and red Scottish beast and the black Welsh runts had already begun. Norden recorded a 'sort of husbandman, or yeoman, rather, who wade in the weeds of gentlemen, who have great feedings for cattle', men who bought the lean stores which were walking into Smithfield, fattened them and brought them back to Smithfield ready for the city tables. There may be detected in the topographer's words the age-old contempt of the corn-grower for the livestock man which survived in the distinction drawn in the twentieth-century directories between farmers and cow-keepers.

The markets of London, and regionally of Bristol and Norwich, York, and the other early Stuart towns, were one great stimulus to contemporary agriculture; and there was a hoard of gold to be tapped by the men who grew the food which the citizens had to have. A new stimulus which was beginning to be important was markets overseas. For some centuries the state had permitted export of grain when supplies were plentiful, and prices therefore low. The government was still primarily concerned that its people should be fed, and its actions were weighted in favour of the consumer and at the expense of the producer; although often the statutes were evaded by rigging the market in reverse and forcing prices down below the level above which exports were prohibited. But Mun was already beginning to turn men's thoughts to a new conception of overseas commerce, as the very title of his book, *England's Treasure by Forraign Trade*, indicated. Gold and silver were gradually becoming synonymous with wealth, and virtues in themselves; and Aristotle's ancient doctrine that the value of money lay only in the good, or bad, use to which it was put was fast losing its hold upon popular economic thought. The new philosophy was a natural corollary of the new conception of the land as one element in the pursuit of personal profit and, therefore, an element in the use of which neither the state nor any other authority had a right to interfere. A man, it was held, might crop his land as freely as he could beat his wife. Both were his own peculiarly private property, and the fundamental relationship of the land to society was becoming obscured by the speed at which the new agrarian pattern was being drawn.

With the disappearance of the medieval ethic the state attempted, with little success, to assume the control of society's relationship with the land. It largely failed because the impetus of economic movement was too strong for it. Influential public thought was ceasing to condemn enclosure for the two great evils which it had formerly been alleged to cause. The last of the statutes to check rural depopulation was passed in 1597, but seems to have been observed only in the breach almost immediately. Only the writers with one foot in the past were concerned with keeping men on the land and continued the campaign in the old spirit and with the old criticisms—Aubrey observed with sorrow that 'for a shepherd and his dogge or a milk mayd can manage that land that upon arable employed the hands of severall scores of labourers'—and the communistic body of Levellers and Diggers, with their doctrine of the common ownership of land, 'bent all their strength to level and lay open enclosures without exercising any manner of violence upon any man's person, goods or cattle'. Their actions and their contention that the land had been stolen by the squires from the people were sympathetically regarded by the great mass of common people in the areas in which they worked, but the strength of the tide of enclosure could never be brushed back by so tiny a broom as theirs.

The second evil with which enclosure had been charged, that of diminishing the supply of bread grain, was shown to be patently false by the steadily rising quantities of corn which came from the land on to the tables of the nation. Population was increasing fast, but the amount of wheat, barley, oats, and rye more than kept pace with it and, indeed, was moving towards a position in which, after the Civil War and Restoration, very considerable quantities were to be available for export. Free enterprise in land use seemed to be abundantly justifying itself, if the eyes of the contemporary observer were focused only upon the results which were being achieved, and were not allowed to glance aside at the victims of the process, the Lazaruses in the rural gutter. It has been calculated that in the 150 years to 1607 about half a million acres in England were transformed from open field and common pasture into land in which the use of a single occupier was absolute and entire. The percentage of enclosed land to the total cultivated land is uncertain because the area of the latter is not accurately known, but it may have reached eight or nine in the Midlands, where the enclosure movement made its most rapid progress. The area of half a million acres may not, in fact, appear very large; but if all the people affected were the small tenants with an average of 10 acres each, then 50,000 families, or a quarter of a million people, or one man in sixteen may have suffered in the process. It is impossible to make any valid calculation on this basis for many reasons: much of the land enclosed, for instance, was in fact only strips in the open fields exchanged, consolidated and fenced, with no harm done to anyone; and many enclosures concerned only the internal rearrangement of a yeoman's holding with no question of a smallholder's being involved. But at least the calculation may indicate that the degree of enclosure was by no means as insignificant as has sometimes been asserted, and that the smoke of the preachers and the pamphleteers was the product of something like a social inferno, a great spiritual and material fire into which small men and small farms which had descended through the centuries were being cast as sacrifices at the altar of progress.

It cannot be denied that the change from the scattered open-field strips and over-stinted pastures, 'pesthouses of disease for cattle, where come the Poor, the Blinde, Lame, Tired, Scabbed, Mangie, Rotten, Murrainous' cattle, sheep and pigs, to enclosed arable and grass, well managed, adequately manured and cropped at will, was an immense one. Without it the improvements in farming which were associated with the introduction of turnips, clovers and artificial grasses would never have been possible, for none of these was amenable to the narrow discipline and conservatism of the open-field farming. At the door of enclosure must lie much of the credit for the increases in crop and stock yield, and therefore of total food supplies, of this time. The forward-looking observer had no doubt whatever of the value of the new system of land held in severalty. Blith, one of Cromwell's captains and a shrewd agricultural commentator, considered that half the arable land of England cultivated under enclosure would produce more than all the arable land farmed in common; and he condemned those who still opposed or neglected to practise enclosure as 'Enemies to the State, of your selves and Common Wealth, so great Abusers of Ingenuity and Good Husbandry'. Blith was a humane man, and he believed that it was possible to enclose the open fields and common pastures of a village without need to 'lay Levell many honest families to the ground, dispeople a whole parish, and send many soules a gooding, a cursed horrible oppression which I would were a Fellony by the Law'. It was, in fact, an offence, but one against a statute which had for decades been a dead letter. It was, however, unfortunately an inescapable result of a general local enclosure that the poor should come off badly.

Yields were rising on these old acres under the impetus of a soaring demand and freedom from the restrictive practices of an outdated communal agriculture. The national granary was also being filled from new acres. The reclamation of the land of Britain had gone on intermittently from the advent of the Saxons, and also, but less rapidly, in the Roman and prehistoric centuries before. It had progressed steadily in Saxon days, and the great medieval prosperity and the commercial exploitation by the monks brought much new land under the plough and under intensive grazing in the twelfth, thirteenth, and early fourteenth centuries. Even during the depression of the 100 years which followed, the peasant can still be traced in the court rolls and manorial accounts as assarting and purpresturing, and winning new acres from waste and forest. The internal peace and prosperity which the Tudors brought accelerated the process of reclamation, and the seventeenth century with its expanding markets and fast-rising returns saw great additions being made to the cultivated land of England. It was a highly remunerative investment for the landlord with a higher rent roll than he could spend in other ways and for the merchant adventurer with his capital gains. The work in the Fens was both the most extensive and the best known. The great swamp, with its dry islets crowned by abbeys, had for centuries had its edges nibbled away by monks and lay improvers; and the reclamation of the whole area had been long debated before the money of the earl of Bedford and the engineering genius of Vermuyden were joined to transform the southern Fens into rich meadows and fertile arable fields which yielded great quantities of meat and grain, fruit, and vegetables.

But while central and southern England was being so vigorously developed, the Celtic borderlands lagged behind. Wales was slowly turning from a wild and lawless land into an amalgam of moderate-sized estates of a small gentry growing upon the English fashion; of a few greater estates; and of an intricate network of family farms held in tenancy or ownership by the men who worked the land in the valleys and upon the lower slopes of the hills. The Scottish borderland found peace even later than Wales, for even at the end of the reign of Elizabeth many men still held land on military tenures and took up arms and rode off on their ponies, more often against the lawless moss troopers, the Doones of the Cheviots, than against Scottish raiders. Both areas were predominantly pastoral and their principal product was livestock. The call of the southern markets reached even the ears of the Scottish and Welsh farmers, however, and the beef beast of Wales, Scotland, and the Cheviots moved southwards in their thousands, finding their food by the wayside and fattened for slaughter upon the pastures of the Home Counties and East Anglia.

The movement of meat on the hoof from the Scottish highland grazings to the markets of the south had its origins in late medieval days, and developed by the seventeenth century into a great annual summer migration from as far afield as the mochairs of Skye and the rich pastures of Islay. The beasts were small, tough, and often aged after years of work. They were ferried over the sea or were towed across tied tail to tail; they gathered at the great trysts of Crieff and Falkirk; and as they were driven south at the rate of ten or fifteen miles a day they fed on the roadside grazings or hired fields. A similar but smaller mass of walking beef came eastwards from Wales. Droving continued until it was killed by the railways, by the hard turnpike roads, and by the improvement of the livestock themselves. The work of the early nineteenth-century breeders made the animals too heavy and too inactive to walk the several hundreds of miles from their homes in the Scottish glens to the grasslands of East Anglia and the Midlands where they were fattened for Smithfield. These older and smaller kyloes from the highlands and the black cattle of Wales formed a very substantial part of the meat supply of London for the two centuries and more during which droving flourished. Indeed, Scotland was, until the agricultural improvements of the latter half of the eighteenth century, little more than a vast rearing ground for English meat; and by the end of this century 100,000 cattle a year were being driven from Scotland to the tables of England. (The whole story is told in Mr. A. R. B. Haldane's recent and authoritative book, *The Drove Roads of Scotland*.)

The face of Britain was being amended in many ways. Stock were peopling the hillsides of the western and northern parts of the island more and more intensively under the incentive of a ready sale to the meat-hungry men of the southern towns. The landscape of open fields was giving place to one of close and pightle hedged with hawthorn or walled with stone. The mad, meandering network of British roads was becoming permanently fixed upon the face of the countryside; and the muddy lanes, twisting and turning as they ran around the headlands of the old open fields now disappearing under enclosure, have become the pleasant byways of rural Britain. The trees in the woods were coming down at a prodigious rate for building, ships, fuel, iron-smelting, and were not being replaced; or were just being cleared to add to the farmed lands: 'what with good husbandry and cleansing of the ground, and what with ill husbandry in felling and selling.' Timber was going so fast, indeed, that the state became anxious at the diminution of its reserves and Spain was being held up as an example of good forestry: for every tree the Spaniard felled, English-men were told, six seedlings must be planted. And, most pregnant with omen for the future, the towns were spilling over the fields which once fed them the houses which were the homes of men who relied upon others to grow the food they ate. British agriculture was meeting the demands for meat, grain, vegetables, and fruit in two ways: by increasing the acreage upon which it was practised, and by raising its efficiency—and both were the natural response to the opportunities of profit which offered themselves. In the result the inefficient, both in methods and men, were going under—the smallholders whose indolent independence was swept from under their feet as their acres in open field and common passed into yeoman or gentlemanly hands; and the communal agriculture which was becoming more and more of an anachronism had to give way to methods of farming which permitted a man to do what he would with his own and take a profit where he could find it. Rural Britain was moving rapidly from one order to another. Medievalism had been killed by slump and sheep, monastic dissolution and a state Church. The state was for some time, however, still sufficiently powerful to continue to impose upon its land and its people some tattered fragments of the old ethics. The Civil War, the Commonwealth, the Restoration, and the deposition of James II all worked to break the paternal despotism of monarchy with its personal concern for the welfare of the citizen, and to replace it with an aristocratic power which flung open the gates to admit uncontrolled enterprise into full authority over commerce, industry, and the fate of men and the land.

CHAPTER FIVE

Protection and the End
of Peasantry

THE CENTURY which followed the restoration of the
Stuart monarchy in 1660 witnessed a remarkable
phenomenon, the rise of the great aristocratic estates.
Its corollary was the decline of the owner-occupier, the
yeoman whose heyday had been the 100 years that ended
with the Commonwealth. In many parishes the yeoman who
owned the land he farmed disappeared entirely. The combination of great estate, the supremacy of the landed classes
and the practical application of mercantile theory that
followed had three very tangible results. Corn laws were
introduced to protect the agricultural producer against
foreign competition; enclosure was pursued at a rapidly

90

increasing rate in order to provide unencumbered land upon which a protected and profitable farming could be followed; and, as an immediate consequence, production continued to grow.

The combination of these factors also had two incalculable but immensely important results. It procured the ejection of the rural proletariat from its few acres which, miserable and ill managed though they too often were, maintained a public in sympathy with its soil; and the sympathy was thereupon turned into distrust and sometimes hate. And it bred a suspicion of agriculture in the urban mind which remains as the greatest enemy of the British farmer. These factors also mark the emergence of rural affairs from medievalism into modernity. They are still with us today, in the same or similar guises: as the place of farming in the national economy, as the extent to which the national interest requires that the producer should be helped at the expense of the consumer, as the means by which more of the nation's mouths may be fed from the nation's own acres, and not least important as the absence of any beneficial interest of the worker in the results of his labour. These vital matters had their origin in the period now under review, that between the return of Charles II to the throne and the death of George II. Many of the burning topics of previous ages—servile services and servile tenures, the stranglehold of the Church upon the land—have ceased to worry men for some centuries. Others —just price, fair shares, a right balance between grassland and arable—have been revived recently. But the major problems of the century between 1660 and 1760 remain so valid and so unsolved today that they merit fuller considertion than has been given to purely medieval bones of contention.

The periodicity of the passage of land from large hands into small and back again has never been fully examined. The cycle of rise of the great consolidated estate reached one peak

—artificially—at the time of Domesday. Thereafter economic circumstances brought about the breakdown of holdings of wide acres into smaller parcels as tenants turned into copyholders, and little freeholders came into possession of areas newly brought into cultivation. This dispersal of the great estate drew towards its climax towards the end of the sixteenth century, when the remaining large landowners found that their ancestors had crippled them by granting away farms on long leases and at rents which remained fixed through a period of soaring prices. The period has a close parallel in the present time, when rents are stabilized and tenancies protected by statute, although the cost of living has risen greatly since the tenancies were granted and the rents fixed. The estate of the earl of Salisbury in 1609 showed a net rental of only £3,856, although the estimated rental value when freed from leases running through several lives was £10,275. The Elizabethan and early Stuart nobility accordingly divested themselves of this unprofitable investment of land ownership, and it has been shown that between 1558 and 1642 the number of manors held by peers in certain Midland areas dropped from 688 to 329. The same period saw the parallel consolidation of the squirearchy on estates of moderate size, and mainly of such new men as prosperous merchants and lawyers who were buying their way into rural society. Harrington, writing at the end of the Commonwealth, even saw the reason for the Civil War in the move of landed property from the conservative, stabilizing hands of the Crown and Church and semi-feudal landowners to a middle-class squirearchy. The power of the Tudor throne had been sufficient to maintain the public interest in food production paramount over the sectional interest of the producer, and to keep the balance in rural society against the aristocracy who owned the land; it was also great enough to keep the new, commercially-minded squirearchy under control. The Restoration saw the direction of movement of land ownership reversed and small estates become consolidated into big ones again because political power had moved from the Crown into upper class hands. The aristocratically inspired land tax fell most heavily upon the small rural *rentier*, and noble influence smoothed the passage through Parliament of the Enclosure Acts which moved the peasants' acres into lordly hands. The result was that by 1780 the owner-occupier of farm land—be he freeholder, copyholder, or lessee for life—had almost passed out of the English scene. In this year the land tax returns showed that only 10 per cent. of the land was still in yeoman hands, and that 90 per cent. was being farmed by tenants. This little handful, one man in ten among the farmers of the country who was still cultivating his own soil, was the surviving remnant of the great band of yeomanry of a century and a half before. Of the manner in which the great landowner cared for the acres he held in trust for the nation something will be said later; it will not always be to his credit, for the Cokes and the Bedfords were somewhat rare birds in the English rural aviary.

During the era of the later Stuarts the aristocratic and landed element in English society achieved and consolidated its domination of Parliament. Nine-tenths of the members of both houses were landlords upon a considerable scale and, indeed, the nominal qualification for a seat in the Commons was a yearly income from a landed estate of not less than £300 a year. The land, therefore, became the key to the door of power as well as that of gentility. The fluidity of the upper strata of rural society, never a closed class, has rarely been more evident than in this period when, as Professor Habakkuk has written, the successful commercial and professional men 'were not so much investing their money in land as buying up the perquisites of a social class, the undisturbed control of the life of a neighbourhood'. Or, as Defoe less kindly put it:

93

Great families of yesterday we show
And lords whose parents were the Lord knows who.

Among the terms on which Charles II came back was the
surrender of the remaining vestiges of the ancient feudal
incidents, of which the chief were the fees from tenants-in-
chief and the proceeds of knight service. The king thereupon
ceased to be the head of a feudal system of land tenure with
its dues as one of the principal sources of his income. In their
place was substituted taxation on modern lines, among which
was the land tax instituted in 1692, originally levied on a
wide variety of income, but soon restricted in practice to that
from rural estates. It was one of those apparently equitable
incidents which in fact press heavily on one class in particular,
and the class of society which it crippled was the small landowners, living entirely upon their rent rolls of a few hundreds
a year and distinguishable from their tenantry only by their
gentility and their coats of arms. The tax brought their
incomes, probably already depleted by compositions with the
Commonwealth, below the lower limit of toleration. Their
answer was to sell out their estates to big neighbours not
dependent entirely upon what their tenants paid them, but
also drawing a revenue from extra-agricultural sources, as
the Bedfords did from their matrimonial alliance with the
merchant prince of the East India Company. This was one
of the two principal factors in the building up of the great
estates which, with their outward and visible sign of the
country seat, were kept virtually intact by the system of
entail until the First World War. The gap between the men of
consequence and the men of no consequence was widening.
The justice of the peace, serving his turn as a county member,
frequented the fringes of fashionable society in London and
acquired Metropolitan culture and affectations. He returned
home to spread a new breadth of outlook into the manor
house, but Hodge and his master remained the plain countrymen whose rough edges were not knocked off until their early

nineteenth century descendants bought pianos for their daughters and furnished drawing-rooms for their wives, to the disgust of Cobbett. Had the decline of the yeomanry been less complete and the schism between landlord and tenantry less deep the men on the land might have shared more in the intellectual and scientific advances of the times, and their heirs been less worthy of the criticism which the Victorian farming reporters bestowed upon their low mentality, their lack of initiative, and their unreasonable opposition to improvement.

To understand the second great factor which gave more land to those who already had an abundance of it, it is necessary to note the fact that the habits of mind of the English were rapidly becoming those of a business nation, and that the time had become one such as Carlyle wrote of, in which cash payment had come to be the sole nexus of man to man. Mun's *England's Treasure by Forraign Trade* was the gospel of the political economist. Trade was the thing, and the Restoration Council of 1660 considered 'how it may be so ordered that we may have more sellers than buyers abroad'. A favourable export-import balance was nearly as great an obsession then as it is today. Not even the land, perhaps least of all the land, was exempted from the drive to turn natural resources into gold and silver. The logical result of this way of thought was the stimulation of exports and the repression of imports, in which policy of protection Britain was by a long stretch the first in the field. Not for more than a century did an Adam Smith arise to point the finger of scorn at a doctrine which conceived of precious metals as the greatest assets of man; only such savages as the Tartar khans and the kings of Prussia hoarded their chests full of treasure.

Agriculture was still the principal industry of the British nation. The men to whom the prosperity of farming brought most profit were the landowners, with their rent rolls which could be pushed up as the returns from produce rose. The landlords were the dominant party in Parliament. It was therefore natural that agriculture should be one of the first to receive the benefits of the policy of protection. It was perhaps a little more than a coincidence that the fashionable doctrines of the political economists should march hand in hand with the self-interest of the landed gentry who were in a position to put precept into practice. The professional agricultural economist of today is often a free trader by conviction; but there is a very strong social argument indeed that at no time in the recent history of Britain has protection been anything but the right policy not only for farming itself, but also in the long run for the nation in its relation to its agriculture. The point is made here, at the beginning of the story of the long dispute between free trade and protection; it will be developed later.

There can be little doubt that the policy of full protection for the British farmer which evolved so rapidly in the second half of the seventeenth century was of benefit to both agriculture and the nation. Within ten years of the Restoration, what restrictions there were on the export of cereals were eased, and before the end of the century they were not only removed, but they had also been replaced by a system of bounties which gave the producer 5s. for every quarter of wheat he sent overseas, 3s. 6d. for rye, and 2s. 6d. for barley. Vigorous protests from the Scottish burghs added an export bounty on oats as well. Davenant wrote at the beginning of the eighteenth century that 'now we export grain of all sorts to Africa, the Canaries, Denmark and Norway, East Country, Flanders, France, Germany, Holland, Ireland, Italy, Madeira, Newfoundland, Portugal, Russia, Scotland, Spain, Sweden, Venice, Guernsey and the English plantations'. The export trade in grain was by modern standards quite insignificant, but it was not the size of the consignments which went overseas which was important, but the stimulus to home production which a ready outlet for surplus crops gave. In the occasional years of scarcity in Britain the old embargoes on export were reimposed and imports were encouraged, but these occasions were rare—only nine years in the period 1689-1765 in fact. The success of this mercantile policy of protection was remarkable. Tudor governments, with a population of something over 3 millions to feed, had been in a constant— but perhaps unnecessary—state of anxiety lest scarcity and famine should come upon the land. In 1700, with the population at nearly 6 millions, Britain was in almost every year producing far more grain than her people could eat, or afford to eat. In the eighteenth century exports of wheat exceeded imports by seven million quarters, barley and malt by 18 million quarters and rye by 1 million quarters. The island was not self-sufficient in oats, but the deficiency was made good by the shipments from Ireland to Liverpool for con- sumption in the new industrial north. In previous centuries the problem of stabilizing grain prices had been insoluble, and fluctuations had been violent from year to year. With the greater margin of production over home demand which protection brought about prices moved less erratically, although the range of variation was still considerable. Nor did the policy raise prices to the home consumer. Through- out the period 1689-1765 the average price of wheat in England has been calculated as being 4*d*. lower than on Continental markets. In the course of these exporting years London developed its great overseas grain market, and the nation's mercantile fleet was aided by the navigation laws which transferred the carrying trade from Dutch to English bottoms.

Mercantilism might have been founded upon principles which displeased a host of later political economists—indeed, Disraeli held that protection was an expedient and not a principle—and their strictures that it interfered with the natural course of commercial development were certainly true. But the saving proviso of many of these economists that

the requirements of defence might outweigh these disadvantages showed that the unique position of land and
agriculture in the national economy was not unrealized—
that the one is not a raw material to be squandered at the
dictates of any flash-in-the-pan policy, or no policy at all,
or the other just another industry with a purely commercial
value; but that the land is a catalyst, irreplaceable and therefore valuable beyond all calculation, which transforms the
labour of the agriculturist into the bread of the nation. And
it might be added, as an addendum to this brief consideration of the early essay in protection, that while the grain
bounties have stolen the historical limelight there were also
important restrictions upon imports of live stock and dairy
produce, with the effect of which upon the development of
the national herd and flock no economist seems yet to have
dealt.

There was thus a formidable combination at work within
Britain: a ruling caste of landed gentry who had everything
to gain from the prosperity of agriculture; a system of
political economy in fashion which permitted the direction
of the national industries into particular channels by financial
stimuli; and a series of statutes, designed by a landed legislature in the light of mercantile theory, to guarantee to
farming the undisputed possession of the home market and to
open foreign markets to British grain. Faced with such an
opportunity, the modern industrialist might sell his soul to
find factory space and a labour force so that he could
multiply his output. The seventeenth- and eighteenth-
century landed reaction was the same; a rush for land, a
determination to keep farm labour cheap and plentiful. It
was rarely that these aims were openly expressed. Indeed,
the new oligarchy of the land clothed in decent patriotic
words the economic forces which were moving them, and
very many of them undoubtedly believed that they were
serving the nation well in what they did—as indeed from one

point of view, that of growing more food, they certainly were.

The urge for more intensive and more profitable farming hid the self-interest that led the leaders of rural society to chafe at the thought of the unenclosed lands which the poor still held, in strips in the open fields, in rights of grazing upon the commons, and in the squatters' holdings on the edge of the wastes. To a man who had caught the fine new fever to farm better, the restrictions of the open-field agriculture which still widely survived and the stubborn, suspicious unprogressiveness of the other partners in the village holdings were intolerable. Public opinion applauded those who sought more land and more freedom to grow more food, and incidentally to make more money. Where enclosure had been condemned by the Tudor moralist as contrary to the common weal, the later Stuart and Hanoverian publicists preached it as a public duty. The change in opinion came from the change in conception of the national good. The medieval statesman had seen a landed peasantry as the most solid of all the foundations of the state, and a share in the soil as a stabilizing factor in society. Arthur Young summed up the older view in his remark that a man will love his country the better even for the land on which to keep a pig. The new philosophy had no time for a civilization which gave the obscure and unimportant men and women of remote villages an hereditary independence; and, in a time when all cultivable land should be cropped for national and personal profit, saw the commons as 'seminaries of a lazy, thieving sort of people' whose inefficient enjoyment of their ancient rights could no longer be tolerated when there were so many new mouths to feed every year and new overseas markets waiting for British grain. And who, even at this distance of time, can say that in the long run that philosophy was wrong?

Whatever one's judgement upon this question, which

Society and the Land

agitated the minds of sociologists and kept the pens of pamphleteers busy over nearly two centuries, the facts remain that the enclosure movement took, in the century and a half from 1700, the whole land of Britain within its compass, so that by the middle of the nineteenth century only a few thousand acres of land held in common survived; so that the rate of production of food upon old and newly enclosed acres grew at a prodigious rate; and so that the landed labourer who formed the bulk of rural society when Charles II returned from France quickly became a landless labourer of a type rarely encountered over the English Channel.

The movement which turned the common lands of Britain into ring-fenced farms may, in its wider agrarian and social aspects, be briefly considered under three headings. First, there was the enclosure of a multitude of tiny $\frac{1}{2}$- and 1-acre strips in the common fields upon which so much of the country's farming was still practised. The case for a re-division of these relics of an archaic system was very strong indeed—it was in fact overwhelming. Strip farming was of use to no one. Such communal cultivations as there may once have been had long since disappeared. The lands could never be properly prepared, neither effectively drained nor cross-ploughed. Rigidity of cropping, although perhaps rarely as restrictive as was once imagined, still compelled the open-field farmers to observe the traditional rotations with only minor variations. Common of shack over the fallow and the stubble perpetuated disease among stock and made the adoption of a progressive livestock breeding policy impossible. Indeed, the disadvantages of a method of farming which had been out of date for centuries had been so patent that in many places voluntary enclosure schemes and the exchange of strips so that a man's holding could be consolidated in one place, fenced, and farmed in severalty had been practised since well before the end of the Middle

Ages. Indeed, the western county of Devon, which has long been thought never to have possessed open fields, has recently been shown to have had such fields, but they were enclosed at a very early date, probably in the twelfth and thirteenth centuries, as men envied and copied the separate enclosures of those of their neighbours who had won new, entire fields from the hills. Of a later age and another county Nathaniel Kent wrote that 'the natural industry of the people is such that wherever a person can get four or five acres together, he plants a white thorn hedge round it, and sets an oak at every rod distance, which is consented to as a kind of general courtesy from one neighbour to another'.

Secondly, there was allied to this voluntary rationalization of the ancient communal arable lands of Britain a doctrine of the efficiency of the large farm. It was a much less valid doctrine in those days, when neither mechanization nor large-scale selling and buying had yet come into being. However, had the majority of people who mattered believed that the medieval conception of a landed peasantry was a true one, it would have been no very difficult matter to see that the man with ten 1-acre strips which were embraced within an eighteenth-century enclosure Act was in a position to continue to farm them as an integrated holding. But the small farm was condemned on both social and economic grounds. 'A farmer of £20 a year is little better than a day labourer', it was written, for 'these small occupiers are a set of very miserable men. They fare extremely hard, work without intermission like a horse, and practise every lesson of diligence and frugality without being able to soften their present lot.' Or, again, 'poverty and ignorance are the ordinary inhabitants of the small farm'. The small farmer was always a poor man, and a poor man is usually a bad farmer. Without capital, he cannot buy the implements for good cultivation, improve the equipment and the condition of his land, buy good seed, stock highly enough or well enough, or have the leisure to plan and the resources to experiment; he is too hard pressed for money to market his produce at the most profitable, and not the earliest, time. In the absence of expensive implements and with the presence of ample and cheap labour, the small farm of the eighteenth century did not have the overriding disadvantage it has today: that it is not big enough to reduce the burden of overhead costs of mechanization to a reasonable figure per acre.

The shrewd observer saw that the small farm was a bad financial investment for the nation. The small farmer was too poor, both materially and often mentally, to take part in the new scientific approach to agriculture and therefore to improve his farming. Such generalizations as these, of course, can be rarely much more than half true; but the experience of many decades, even centuries, has shown that the small arable holding is often uneconomic both to the nation and to the man who cultivates it, unless market-garden crops needing close and constant work and returning a high profit per acre can be grown. But the small farm which produces milk, pig meat, or other produce of livestock can be a highly efficient unit—except, of course, that the man who does a 20-acre livestock farm well is soon moving into one of 200 acres. It is for this reason that the tiny holding has survived, and should still survive, in the pastoral counties, while it is nearly extinct in the arable areas of the east and south.

These provisos which take the small livestock farm outside the field of condemnation of the small farm in general and of arable strip farming in particular belong more logically to the third heading under which these questions of eighteenth- and nineteenth-century enclosure are being considered— that of the partition of the commons into separate, in- dividually held fields. Few of these commons remain today, and then mainly in towns where public opinion was strong enough to enforce the preservation of an open space, or on soils so infertile that it has never been worth anyone's while to bother about them. In the eighteenth and earlier centuries the common, unenclosed, and unimproved pasture was the great reservoir of the land of the village, a territorial heritage upon the acres of which the rural poor could pursue some semblance of their hereditary calling. It fed the widow's cow and the pauper's ducks; and the swine of the squatter rooted round the shack which its owner had built upon a few roods filched from the edge of the green. The 'starved, tod-bellied runts neither fit for the dairy nor the yoke', were objects of contempt in the eyes of the improver, and the commons themselves were an eternal temptation to the agrarian potentates of the village who believed that they could make far better use of the land, as indeed agriculturally they could. A reporter to the Board of Agriculture called one of this class a professional farmer, in contradistinction to the peasant who followed an inherited, traditional art from habit rather than by deliberate choice. Socially, these miserable, overstocked and uncared-for acres were one of the only two links between a decayed peasantry and complete pauper-dom. The other was the domestic industries, of which spinning, carding, and weaving were the early examples.

Enclosure as it was known at this period was a parlia-mentary process by which the arable strips in the common fields and the pastoral acres on the commons were thrown into the melting pot, to emerge as integrated holdings each capable of being fenced off from all other land in the village, and in theory equitably parcelled out between all who had held rights over land in the ancient system. This method of enclosure by Act of Parliament initiated in the eighteenth century embraced more than $6\frac{1}{2}$ million acres, or one-fifth of the area of England. In much of the process the poorer strata of society had no say. They were an inarticulate, unenfranchised class who could formulate their claims only with the greatest difficulty. In many cases they were ignorant of the precise nature of their rights; they and their fathers before them had always kept a cow and some geese on the common, but by what first authority, if any, they knew not. Usually the promoters of the Act, in most cases the lord of the manor and his larger tenants, took no steps to bring the proposals to their notice. And when the Bill came before Parliament the commoners, even if they knew of it, had neither the wit nor the means to oppose it by petition. Finally, when the Act was passed the enclosure commissioners who executed it and who had virtually absolute powers in the redistribution of the land, were often the bailiffs of the landowners who had promoted the Act. Young, in his early days, was no enemy to enclosure; but he wrote that 'the property of proprietors, and especially of the poor ones, are entirely at their [the commissioners'] mercy: every passion of resentment and prejudice may be gratified without control, for they are invested with a despotic power known in no other branch of business in this free country'. The Hammonds, in their classic *Village Labourer*, added: 'it would be interesting to know how much of England was appropriated on the initiative of the lord of the manor acting under the authority given him by the High Court of Parliament.'

Allotments were made to the small landowners of the village, but few of them were able to retain their land. The costs of the enclosure process were often heavy, in some cases up to £12 an acre; fencing and farm roads were an intolerably costly burden to a man of little or no means; and the Church characteristically saw to it that the financial costs to which the ecclesiastical properties were put were added to those of the little commoners. By no means all Acts of enclosure were initiated so selfishly, administered so harshly, or ended so tragically for the little proprietor; but the selfishness, the harshness and the tragedy were often enough present to justify the application to the movement in general of the phrase, the greatest land-grab in British history. It was a land-grab in which the motive force was the great eighteenth-century class of landed gentry; and while the landed gentry were often moved by a genuine desire for agricultural improvement, there is little doubt that they were moved even more often by the need to replenish the coffers which had been emptied at the gaming tables or to restore the fortune of an entailed estate upon which too many mortgages had been raised for the dowries of daughters. The degree of misery which these enclosures brought with them has never been satisfactorily assessed. Most contemporary observers had too many political axes to grind to be impartial. Modern economic historians have been too much swayed by their sympathies and antipathies to be just to both sides. And it is not easy to translate such statistics as are available into terms of human suffering. Some conclusions at the two extremes can, however, be accepted without reservation. Enclosure was necessary in the particular circumstances of that time if a growing nation was to be fed, for even if the premise that cereal production on a small farm is as high per acre as that on a large farm is accepted, it is difficult to see how the produce from a multitude of tiny holdings could either be brought under the influence of technical advances or, once grown, how it could be economically brought to the urban table. At the other extreme, the poverty which followed in the train of the loss of the commons was very considerable indeed.

The enclosure movement added its quota to the army of workless which had been growing from century to century. At some time in the past the balance between the work to be done and the people who were there to do it had been upset. In so far as each man grew what food and made what tools and clothes he needed, primitive society had achieved the perfect balance in employment. That happy equilibrium was lost when society became civilized, in the exact sense of that word. Rural population expanded faster than new opportunities as master or man in farming arose, and the

surplus men and women moved into urban jobs. The exodus
from the land was, as it has usually been since, the result of
lack of rural opportunity as much as the glitter of the town.
By the time of the eighteenth-century enclosures a very large
number of families maintained a precarious existence in the
British countryside by clinging to the hems of the commons.
Arthur Young quoted the case of the small village of Blofield
in Norfolk, where on 39¾ acres on the edge of a 700-acre
heath 30 families of squatters maintained 23 cows, 18 horses
and some donkeys, pigs, geese, and poultry. At Culmstock in
Devon the manor had 400 acres of commons where there
were 'nine dwelling houses lately built upon the wast by
severall poore men who holde the same without any lease or
payment of rent'. When these and the tens of thousands of
their fellows were thrown landless upon the chill eighteenth-
century world, they had to wait for some decades before
British industry developed enough to absorb some of them.
Population, then, for centuries before and ever since had
been running ahead of opportunities of employment, except
in such periods of hot or cold war through which we have
recently been passing, when the armament needs of the
state create an artificially high level of work to be done.

It was, however, the publicly avowed belief of many
eighteenth-century political economists that a high degree
of insecurity of employment was the surest way of maintaining a labour force for farming which was both adequate and
cheap. Bishton, who wrote the report on Shropshire farming
for the Board of Agriculture towards the end of the eighteenth
century, said bluntly that when the commons were enclosed
the labourers 'will work every day in the year, their children
will be put out to work early . . . and that subordination of
the lower ranks of society which in the present times is so
much wanted would be thereby considerably secured.' The
antithesis of subordination was the independence which the
occupation of even a little plot of land gave to a man: it was

his insurance against starvation in time of unemployment or dispute with his master. 'The only way to make the labourers temperate and industrious,' said William Temple, 'is to lay them under the necessity of labouring all the time they can spare from meals and sleep in order to procure the common necessaries of life.' The economic theorists, who saw low wages as the basis of a favourable balance of trade, wrote many pamphlets containing specimen budgets for the labourer, budgets which illustrated the lowest level of nutrition at which he might be expected to be able to do a day's work and rear a brood of children to replace him when he wore out: the thrifty dairy farmer rations his cows on the same basis today. The poor rural workman was no longer a fellow countryman but a member of a separate species—'the lower orders, the labouring poor, the meaner sort'. This view lasted for two centuries: Mr. Bertrand Russell has recalled the Duchess of Cleveland of his acquaintance who, outraged by bank holidays, exclaimed: 'What do the poor want with holidays? They ought to work.'

The number of those who earned the bulk of their living by working for others is difficult to ascertain until recent days. In his estimate of 1688 Gregory King put the number of families of labouring people and out-servants at 364,000 and of cottagers and paupers at 400,000; and the two together accounted for nearly half the whole population of the nation. If it may be assumed that almost all these men, women and children were fast losing what little independence they once had and that the bulk of them still lived and worked in agriculture or one of its ancillary trades, then the seeds of despair of betterment, of hatred for the master in husbandry and his master the landlord, and of disillusionment with Chalkhill's 'sweet contentment of the countryman' were being sown very widely indeed. British agriculture has been reaping the springen cokkel ever since; and British literature has, until recent times, ignored the miseries of rural life and caught only at the simplicity of the bucolic shepherd and the innocence of the rosy-cheeked dairymaid.

There were, of course—even in the eighteenth century—some few humanitarians who saw the depth of the evil that was being done; men who could appreciate the immensity of the advance in agrarian method which enclosure made possible but could also realise the social evil of divorcing a peasant people from its ancestral soil. The author of *A Political Enquiry into the Consequences of Enclosing* pointed out that 'there are village people, such as the cottager, the mechanic, and inferior shopkeeper to whom common rights are an incitement to industry. Their children, sent out to yearly service among the farmers, manage in time to scrape together £20 or £30, marry young women possessed of an equal sum, obtain a cottage, and purchase cows, calves, sheep, hogs and poultry. Then while the husband hires himself out as a day labourer, the wife stops at home and herds the livestock on the common. Out of the former's wages the rent of the cottage, orchard and two or three acres of meadow ground is paid which, save for the rights of common, would be insufficient to support the beasts and poultry of which his property consists. How would this class be provided for if the commons were ploughed up?' The idyll of industrious husband, thrifty and hard-working wife, the prosperous stock and the full use of the few acres of land may have been the picture of an idealist; but it cannot be denied that the opportunity of independence and advancement which was once there was being removed. There were many plans for remedying some of the evils. David Davies urged that land should be given to the cottager for a cow, a plot of potatoes, and a saleable crop such as flax or hemp; and that the wide wastes should be broken up into smallholdings. Nathaniel Kent anticipated the later battle-cry of three acres and a cow by many decades: 'Capable labourers should have larger cottages . . . and a small portion of pasture land of about three acres to enable the occupier to support a cow.' Even the Board of Agriculture, in the closing years of the eighteenth century, submitted general enclosure Bills to Parliament which provided for permanent allotments of land for local labourers; but their scheme was considered to be 'too generous to the poor'. Adam Smith also saw the social evils which flowed from mercantilism pursued to extremes— 'a plentiful subsistence increases the bodily strength of the labourer', he wrote, 'and the comfortable hope of bettering himself and of ending his days in perhaps peace and plenty animates him to exert that strength to the utmost. Where wages are high, accordingly, we shall always find the workmen more active, diligent and expeditious than when they are low.'

But wages, in fact, were too often at or even below the starvation point, in spite of the general prosperity of agriculture. The Berkshire budgets of labourers' families which Davies published all showed a yearly deficiency before even all the bare necessities of life had been bought. The plight of the labourer in husbandry was worst where agriculture was the only occupation to be had. In the West Country, where the cloth industry had decayed, the level of subsistence was distressingly low. In the north, on the other hand, where new industry had higher and steadier wages to offer and the farm employer had to pay his men adequately in order to keep them, there was a comparative prosperity among the rural labouring classes.

This must be said, however, in defence of the agricultural employer: the wages paid by him were not generally expected to be the only money going into the cottages. Wives and children had, in the past, made the family ends meet by putting into the kitty what they could earn, sometimes in farm work, but more often in the domestic industries, of which the processing of wool had been one of the earliest and the most important. But these occupations were, one by

one, taken into the factory. Almost the last of them to go—
and this is trespassing far into the nineteenth century—was
the cottage industry of straw-plaiting. Women plaited over
the kitchen pot, the garden gate or the cradle; boys plaited
as they scared the crows off the corn; even the men worked
simple patterns as they tended cattle on the common. Busy
fingers working long hours could make much money. Young
met a girl in Hertfordshire who earned a guinea a week with
her straw 'cheens', which was about three times as much as
the sum her father brought home from his work on the farm.
The loss of these auxiliary earnings was all the more important in that farm wages, apart from the deflationary
influence of the mercantilists, had fallen further and further
behind the cost of living as one century followed another.
Wheat is not an entirely valid criterion, because wheaten
bread came into use among the poor only gradually; but
with that qualification in mind it may be remarked that
while the average farm wage of late Elizabethan days would
have bought 128 pints of wheat, the weekly wage of a
labourer in the closing years of the eighteenth century
would have purchased only 66 pints. Another computation
suggests that between the end of the sixteenth century and
the end of the eighteenth century agricultural wages rose by
only 50 per cent. Many workers—the unmarried ones—lived
in, of course, and as they received much of their recompense
in kind, seated with the farmer at his own table and
sharing in the better living of the times, their lot was an
incomparably better one than that of the man who lived
out.

The disease from which the British countryside was
suffering was a widening of the chasm between the rich and
the poor. On the one hand the rent-taker, the farmer with
his profits, the tithe-owner were becoming richer and richer.
On the other, the working classes were starving; and their
miseries were driving them into crime. Material production,

however, of cereals, meat, and other foods was reaching a sturdy adolescence. The mental outlook of the late Stuart age was a propitious one for agricultural improvement. Vigorous minds were released from the endless theological disputations which had wasted the good brains of previous ages and, in place of 'seeking the divine truth in the quasi-historical records of an ancient Hebrew people', they were able to study divinity through the divine works which were on every hand. Sir Thomas Browne had long before remarked that God preferred a learned admiration of His works to the gross rusticity which looked at Nature without comprehension, interest, or question. Countless generations of farmers had folded sheep and carted muck on to their land, and had accepted the fertility which followed without seeking to discover how it came. Now Digby was analysing the effect of nitrogen on the soil; Grew with his microscope was turning plant physiology from folk lore into a science; the Georgical Committee of the Royal Society were attempting to compile a detailed survey of English husbandry; and Tull was seeking to adapt an ancient theory of elemental forces to a new empirical inquiry into the properties of goodness in the earth. The conclusion to which Tull's reasoning brought him was wrong, but the important thing was that he and his fellows were thinking at all about the matters which before had been taken for granted.

Right through the range of agricultural practice—and in almost every other sphere of industry as well—the light of calculating inquiry was illuminating the path to better farming. But it was naturally a very long time before the proved ideas of the men in the vanguard of agricultural thought reached and were adopted by the rearguard in the remote fields. The alternate husbandry of Blith, the discoveries of Digby of the virtues of nitrogenous fertilizers, even the extravagant wastefulness of pouring good fodder down the mouths of poor cows against which Fitzherbert

fulminated in the days of Henry VIII, are even now matters
to which it is necessary for authority to draw the attention of
the more backward farmers. Blith's 'mouldy old leavened
husbandmen who calumniated and depraved every new
invention', were not altogether to be blamed for their
conservatism, for pseudo-science and extravagance of claim
were even more rife in agriculture in the seventeenth century
than they are today. But as new crops such as potatoes and
turnips and more nutritious species of grasses, new stock such
as the ancient breeds of cattle improved by crossing with
animals from the Low Countries, new implements such as
the lighter ploughs, horse-hoes and the earliest drills percol-
ated downwards, so the amount of food in meat, milk, and
grain produced from every acre rose. Scientific agriculture
was still far in the future, but an enlightened empiricism was
leading the husbandmen of Britain towards better things.
The prerequisite of progress was enclosure. However much
one may deplore its social consequences and the miseries
and the hardening of the public heart which accompanied
it, one must admit that. The result of enclosure for the
tenant was usually a rise in the rent he had to pay. But
except in times of agricultural slump high rents are no bad
thing, as Houghton noted in this period. 'The rack renter',
he said, 'puts them upon new industry and products', which
the husbandmen had neglected before because their rent was
small and their livelihood easily earned.

This chapter has dealt briefly with the impact upon agriculture of the national policies and social patterns of the
century or so which followed the Restoration. Some attempt
must now be made to show how farming responded to the
stimuli of a rapidly growing home market wholly reserved
to itself; of foreign markets actively opened to its produce;
of cheap labour and improving methods employed upon
wider, more conveniently aggregated, and individually
controlled acres. The area upon which grain farming and

pastoral pursuits were being intensified was drawing near in size to that in modern Britain: that is, the area which it is economical to use in normal times. At the end of the seventeenth century Davenant estimated the area in pasturing and meadow at 12 million acres. The 1951 figure was 14 million acres of temporary and permanent grass. The difference of 2 million acres is elusive. Davenant's figure was only an intelligent guess, and the dividing line between permanent grass and moorland is elastic; but the principal part of the variation was undoubtedly due to the improvement of part of the remaining waste lands of the nation into good grazing, and particularly in the pastoral areas of the north and west where assarting in the seventeenth and eighteenth centuries was more than doubling the area of a large number of holdings. It is almost impossible to correlate the earlier estimates of the extent of these waste lands with the present figures. Gregory King in 1696 estimated the barren lands of England and Wales at 10 million acres; in 1795 the report of the committee of the Board of Agriculture stated that nearly 8 million acres were uncultivated. The land survey of 1942-6 gave the area of rough grazing as a little over $5\frac{1}{2}$ million acres, and in addition nearly 7 million acres were unaccounted for as being in other than agricultural use. In all today nearly $12\frac{1}{2}$ million acres of land are of low or no production. The earlier figures are obviously not wholly reliable, but in the matter of the extent of land use there appears to be a tendency to underrate the achievements of the past. Indeed, the agricultural observers of all centuries have been critical of the neglect by contemporaries of large areas of land, but they dealt and still deal in figures and not in realities. Young, for instance, in his *Observations on the Present State of Waste Lands of Great Britain* (1773), pointed to the 600,000 acres which were unused in Northumberland, and as many more in Cumberland and Westmorland; but even today there are 500,000 acres of mountain and moorland in

Northumberland and 510,000 in Westmorland and Cumberland which are, from their inherent infertility, very thinly stocked indeed.

But although the area which is being farmed may not have changed a very great deal in the last 250 years, yet the agriculture which has been practised on these acres has become far more intensive and far more productive. The intensification of farming got really under way during the eighteenth century, under the stimuli of great home and overseas markets for grain and a rapidly growing demand for meat. The population of England and Wales, which had stood at about four million in 1600, had risen to 5,800,000 by 1700 and to 6,320,000 by 1750. It rose by leaps and bounds thereafter. Again using Davenant's figures—and, dubious though they may be, they are all we have—the nation was at the end of the seventeenth century producing 14 million bushels of wheat, 10 million of rye, 27 million of barley and 16 million of oats. In 1764 Charles Smith estimated production at 30 million bushels of wheat, 8 million of rye, 35 million of barley and 34 million of oats. The 1951 figures are 90 million bushels of wheat, 32 million of rye, 70 million of barley, and 60 million of oats. In addition, the arable lands of England and Wales are today growing 228 million bushels of potatoes and enough sugar beet to provide the whole of the domestic ration of sugar. Expressed tabularly, and using the starch equivalent of the various commodities as a common yardstick, home production of food has risen in the manner shown in the table on p. 115.

Again, in the sphere of livestock, it is quite impossible to assess accurately the extent of the improvement begun in the eighteenth century. Stock numbers have risen. Davenant estimated the cattle population of England and Wales at the end of the seventeenth century at $4\frac{1}{2}$ million head, of sheep 12 million, and of pigs 2 million. The 1951 figures are 7·9 million for cattle, 12·4 million for sheep, and 2·9 million for

PRODUCTION INDEX[1]
Starch equivalent of millions of bushels,
England and Wales

	End of seventeenth century	1764	1951
Wheat	10·08	21·61	73·8
Rye	7·20	5·72	23·04
Barley	19·18	24·81	49·70
Oats	9·61	20·47	36·0
Potatoes	0	?	37·74
Total	46·07	72·61	220·28
Population	5,800,000	6,500,000	45,000,000
Production *per capita*	7·94	11·17	4·9

pigs. The comparison does not end here, however, for the weight of meat and milk produced per head of stock has risen, and the rate of turnover has also increased. The work of the predecessors of Bakewell and the Collings in stock improvement, unpublicized and unknown as it is, is evident in the return of weights from Smithfield market alone. Where in 1710 the market was receiving beef beasts of an average of 370 lb., these beasts were in 1795 weighing about 800 lb. Sheep weights jumped from 28 lb. to 80 lb., and lamb weights from 18 lb. to 50 lb. And animals were not only reaching far heavier weights, but they were reaching them far more quickly, at three years of age in the case of beef beasts instead of at five or six as a century before.

Agriculture was now become a completely industrial enterprise. The enormous increase in home food production

[1] This table is intended to be only a rough illustration of the progress of farming. It is, I think, that. But it can, of course, be faulted at every point as an accurate expression of the net yield of agriculture; for example, it omits all livestock and livestock products, and disregards the external material, e.g. artificial fertilizers, put into the soil.

was very largely due to this fact. And farming was regarded as much as a source of profit to the nation as the provisioner of the national larder. The aristocratic landlords had become preference shareholders in a great agrarian concern, with the power to direct national policies towards profitable ends. The tenant farmers had become the managers with substantial holdings in ordinary shares, but subject to arbitrary dismissal. The village labourer was divorced from all material interest in his employment and from all social responsibility; and the little family factories in the open fields which he had inherited had been taken from him and absorbed in the greater agricultural enterprises. Efficiency was being slowly won at the expense of some injustice and much human misery. The stage was obviously setting for some considerable social upheavals in the next few generations.

CHAPTER SIX

Schism between Town and Country

UNTIL THE passing of the first corn laws in the second half of the seventeenth century, the nation regarded the interest of the native consumers of its agricultural produce as paramount. The legislation then evolved and later developed through the eighteenth century sought to hold a just balance between the man who grew bread corn and the man who ate it. The end of the Napoleonic Wars saw a radical change brought about, to the benefit of the producer and to the real or imaginary harm of both the domestic consumers and the nascent export industries of

Britain. But whatever else they did, the series of corn laws which extended over a century and three-quarters made smooth the passage between the first and second of the three great periods of British agriculture—that in which the medieval farmer grew only what he and his neighbours in the local towns needed; that in which production ran ahead of the increase in population, and without the encouragement of cereal exports the farmer would have been left with surpluses unsold and on his hands; and that in which population outstripped production and the nation imported food, first to supplement and then largely to replace what could be grown at home.

It would be both tedious and unnecessary to trace in detail the history of the corn laws. Legislation attempted throughout the whole period to keep abreast of the alterations in the economic structure of the nation by ringing the changes; upon controlled and uncontrolled exports with and without bounties upon the grain sent abroad; and upon absolute or conditional prohibition of imports, with such variations in the import duties on overseas grain as were considered to be appropriate to the times. But all the time the objects which the legislature had in view were commendable ones. The home production of grain was to be raised to a pitch at which there would be always enough for the nation's own needs, so that it might become self-sufficient in times of war. Only little less minor aims were that the large rise in price which had followed only a slight deficiency should be avoided, and that the disastrous fall in price which arose from any unsaleable surplus should be obviated by giving the farmer a market for all he grew. This was to be accomplished by offsetting, by means of the export bounty, the cost of transport of produce overseas and any difference between British and foreign prices. It was a policy which set the example, though for a different reason, for the American and other foreign expedients of undercutting and dumping of later times.

But towards the end of the eighteenth century it became obvious that the farmer was falling behind in his race with a soaring population. Hopes of keeping Britain entirely fed with her own bread grains gradually began to be abandoned. In many years more grain was imported than was exported; and the coincidence of bad harvests and war brought about a scarcity that was near to famine and prices that ran at a fabulously high level for twenty years. But even in peacetime foreign grain was not to be had in sufficient quantity, for with the British market closed to them so often by import restrictions, Continental growers lacked the incentive to produce regular surpluses for British use; and when the weather caused the home crop to fail the European crop was nearly always short.

In spite of their occasional failures to reach the theoretical objectives, the corn laws went some way towards succeeding in their purpose of preventing 'grain from being at any time either so dear that the poor cannot subsist or so cheap that the farmer cannot live by growing of it'. The British farmer, during the periods of high price in the Napoleonic Wars in particular, rushed into an arable agriculture almost irrespective of the fitness of his land for the plough; and, with wheat maintaining a steady 120s. the quarter against a pre-war average around 45s., large profits were made. When the wars ended Brougham said that 'not only have wastes disappeared . . . giving place to houses, fences and crops but even the most inconsiderable commons, the very village greens and the little strips of sward by the wayside been cut up into cornfields in the rage for farming.'

The succession of Acts from the late seventeenth century onwards which had sought to secure a sufficient supply of bread grain met some sporadic opposition; but in general public hostility was aroused only in the worst periods of scarcity, and it subsided immediately upon a good harvest. It took the marriage of the antagonism against the defiantly

protectionist Act of 1815 and the leadership of the new
commercial middle class to conceive and give birth to a
sustained and eventually successful campaign against the
system of the regulation of the international trade in grain.
The 1815 Act has been commonly described as a blatant
attempt by the landed classes who still ruled Britain to make
permanent in peace the high grain prices of war; and it is
true that it included the absolute prohibition of imports of
wheat when the home price was below 80s. a quarter. But
costs of production were high, which went some way
towards justifying the high level at which the ports could be
opened to foreign grain; and there was more than a little
truth in the plea by Liverpool, the Tory prime minister, that
the Act was not an attempt to protect the landlord, but was
intended to secure a regular domestic supply to the native
consumer. In the event, it did succeed in maintaining
production in all years of reasonably full crops and good
harvest weather at a level which fed, or nearly fed, the people
of Britain well into the nineteenth century.

The opposition to agricultural protection came then, as it
has come ever since, from the classes who saw the land merely
as a mere instrument of production, another of the machines
which were turning out textiles and steam engines, to be used
when the national interest required it, but at all other times
to be laid aside as redundant and allowed to tick over un-
remuneratively or to go out of use altogether. British
agriculture, it was agreed, was a vital weapon in time of war,
an insurance against famine; but the Victorian man of
commerce thought the premium too high for the cover it
provided. He argued with Ricardo—although forgetting
Ricardo's reservation in favour of some agricultural protection—that to prohibit competition from foreign grain meant
that the price level at which home-grown wheat ran was
high because it was immune from normal economic forces.
And he further argued that a high price for bread meant that

higher wages had to be paid to enable the skilled artisan or the unskilled labourer to live: high wages maintained the prices of British goods at a level above that of the foreign manufacturer: and Britain's export trade—her 'treasure', as Mun had called it long ago—suffered accordingly.

But the objection to agricultural protection had another facet. International trade must be reciprocal. As a French peasant told Sir Edward Bowring in the 1830's, 'Admit our corn and then we will see whether anybody can prevent the importation of your manufactures into France. We are millions, willing to clothe ourselves in the garments you send us, and you have millions of hungry mouths to take our corn.' At the time, and for many decades afterwards, Britain had everything to gain commercially from free trade. Her industries were far in advance of those of any other country, foreign markets were wide open to receive goods from the factories of London and the industrial north. And, as the events turned out, British agriculture had nothing to fear from free trade at that particular time. When protection was removed by the repeal of the corn laws the average price of wheat continued to run at much the same level as before for another quarter of a century, thereby proving to be false the arguments of the liberal economists that prohibition of imports below a certain price level was the first link in the chain of high wages. The truth was, and it was there for them to have seen, that British and Continental prices ran closely together. Although the standards of living of the British farmer and even of the farm labourer were above those of the European peasant still enslaved in the ancient bonds of feudalism, the transport costs from, say, Dantzig to London more than outweighed any difference in costs of production of the heavy British crops of wheat grown with comparatively dear labour and the lighter Polish crops cultivated and harvested by people still close to slavery. It was not until American corn began to pour in that the British farmer found his own market weighted against him; and when Repeal was in the air none dreamed that the Americas were destined to become one of the great granaries of the world. 'With respect to the corn trade of the United States,' McCulloch wrote in a tract of 1841, 'it is abundantly certain that we need not look to that quarter for any considerable supplies.' In fact, 'within the last half-dozen years considerable quantities of flour have been shipped from Dantzig to other European ports for America'. O unprophetic man! Ten years later the danger was being dimly realized by wiser men, among them Caird, who wrote that 'with the extension of railways and steam navigation there seems good reason to anticipate the permanence of a low range of prices'. Even in 1861, when the well-informed *Scottish Farmer* lifted its editorial eyebrows over the rise of wheat imports to 6 million quarters in 1860, there was little inkling of the flood that was to come; and the editor found a matter of both 'surprise and pride in the energies of the profession and the resources of science which in the face of such an invasion can maintain prosperity and increase'. Poor man, he could not have foreseen such an occasion as that on the morning of 1 October 1888, when the London Corn Exchange dealt in 60,160 quarters of wheat of which only 440 quarters were home-grown.

In their closing years the corn laws became the field of battle between the old landed nobility and the new commercial riches. The defiant protectionism of the Act of 1815 caused the evil mark of monopolism, the crown of thorns for so long and so unjustly worn by the miller and the corn merchant, now to be perceived upon the brow of the rural landlord. The fight was to all intents and purposes a straight one between commerce and the landowner. The other parties who had once had so deep an interest in the prosperity of the British countryside, the commoners and squatters and the part-time farm labourers who earned the rest of their livings in domestic industries, had been swept away in the wave of rural depopulation. The landlord was now supported in his struggle for British corn for British people only by his tenant farmers and by the Chartists, who saw in agricultural protection the full employment for the rural workers which would keep them out of the towns and out of competition for urban jobs. Neither Melbourne's plea that 'to leave the whole agricultural interest without protection I declare before God that I think it the wildest and maddest scheme that has ever entered into the imagination of man to conceive', nor the spate of Tory pamphlets, convinced the business man of Manchester that the great country landowners were anything but parasites upon the body economic. 'The rent of land,' Adam Smith wrote, 'is naturally a monopoly price. It is not at all proportioned to what the landlord may have laid out upon the improvement of the land, or to what he can afford to take; but to what the farmer can afford to give.'

It was unfortunate that the contemporary facts often justified the free traders in their view; for it was only too easy to find a landowner who took the cash in rent and let the credit of estate improvement go. It is a point which will be returned to later in this chapter. The free trade theorists could also go back a quarter of a century to Malthus and read that the ideal of self-sufficiency in grain was an economically unsound one, for the price of English corn was kept high because much poor land had to be drawn into cultivation in order to keep the people fed, and this land was in fact used only under the impetus of a domestic closed market and artificially sustained prices. It was, indeed, alleged to have been one of the virtues of the protectionist Act of 1815 that it saved from destruction the capital invested by owners and tenants in the marginal lands of Britain. Again on the short view the free traders had common sense on their side. Why pour money into the Shropshire hills or the sour acres of Exmoor to grow at great expense small crops of wheat which could be bought far more cheaply from France or Scandinavia? It was forgotten that it had been the produce from these same poor acres which had saved Britain from starvation in the Napoleonic Wars. The national memory in such matters is incredibly short, and was—and is —sometimes made the shorter by the refusal of the farmer to compromise with necessity.

The Anti-Corn Law League, begotten by Cobden upon the lusty damsel of commercialism, had as its purpose during its short active life from 1838 to the Repeal in 1846 the release of the country from the monopoly of the landlords, of industry from what was deemed to be the stranglehold of the high bread price, high wage complex, and of the working classes from dear food. Thackeray drew for the League his famous cartoon of soldiers of the Landlord State repulsing the Russian and the Pole who came with corn for a starving British family; and the League's journal poured scorn upon agricultural inefficiency, which was no more difficult to find than the profiteer landlord. 'We have a right,' its article said, 'to demand that the same degree of science, industry, capital and enterprise shall be applied to land which have been so successfully devoted to manufactures.' It was as well that the League's leader-writers did not add humanity to the quartet of commercial virtues. The protectionists' reply was an Anti-League, the child of Robert Baker, an Essex tenant farmer. It was bound to fail not only because of the strength of feeling among the new middle-class electorate against the corn laws, but also because it was itself ill organized and leisurely, and was supported only reluctantly and half-heartedly by aristocratic landlords, who scorned to participate in democratic politics. Even the agricultural interest was divided. George Hope, tenant of Fenton Barns, one of the best farmers in Britain, and an honest-minded man, argued for Repeal because 'the future of agriculture depended on cherishing the welfare of the largest possible number of consumers'. It was a highly commendable motive, but it would have been discreet to advance it only if agriculture had been sufficiently organized to ensure that the producers' interests had an equal hearing with the consumers'; and agriculture was not to be so organized for another 100 years.

The corn laws which had protected the British cereal market in favour of the British corn-grower for a century and a half succumbed at last to the combination of Anti-Corn Law League pressure, the political perceptiveness of Peel, and the potato famine in Ireland. Peel saw that national self-sufficiency in bread corn was rapidly becoming a less and less tenable objective. Although the country had nearly reached it in eight good harvest years out of fourteen before the Repeal in 1846, the expansion of population and industry alike demanded on the current assessment complete freedom of trade, for Britain was playing a game of international commerce in which she thought she must always hold all the aces. The growing crisis was precipitated by the failure of the Irish potato crop and the necessity of opening British ports to foreign grain to feed the starving Irishman; and once opened the ports could, in the light of public opinion, hardly be closed again. The Duke of Wellington, in one of his irascible explosions, swore that 'Rotten potatoes have done it all; they have put Peel in his damned fright'. In fact, Peel was a man unusually honest in his mind, and he clearly believed that he was doing right by his country, although his action might neither please his own Tory Party nor be of advantage to his own position. He certainly expected prices to fall; and when Caird, *The Times'* agricultural correspondent, visited his estate four years after Repeal and shortly after Peel's death he found that the late prime minister had made arrangements for the tenantry at Tamworth to cushion upon his own purse the effects of his action, which he expected to be 'to maintain a low range of prices of corn in average seasons, and to prevent very high prices in seasons of dearth'. He promised that he would set aside one-fifth of his rent roll to spend on such improvements as would enable his tenants to meet home competition; and much of this money was spent on manures given for application on the farms on his estate. Peel, of course, was not entirely disinterested in his benevolence, for in helping his tenants in this way he was improving his own lands as well as ensuring the maintenance of his rent roll.

As has been indicated, the British corn-grower was not immediately ruined by the throwing open of the nation's ports to foreign grain. Population was growing so fast that the corn market absorbed all that was grown at home or sent by the very limited transport from overseas. The *Scottish Farmer* commented in 1847 that 'including imports from America, the available supplies of home-grown wheat have been about adequate to meet the wants of the population'. There was no undue fall in price. In the twenty-five years after Repeal wheat prices ranged between 74s. 8d. and 38s. 6d. a quarter, and averaged 52s. 9d.; in the twenty-five years before Repeal they varied from 70s. 8d. to 39s. 4d. and averaged 60s. 1d. Peel's gamble, therefore, had done little harm to the agricultural industry, taking one year with another; and had also had little effect in stabilizing prices. The Old World was living too near the bone and was all subject to too much the same climate to make much difference between prices in a national and an international trade in grain.

Two points emerge from these century-old debates which are pertinent today, and which may be briefly noted here while they are fresh in mind. By jettisoning the protection of home-grown grain, the man of commerce who had overborne the landed government of the day committed Britain to what has now been more than a century of utter dependence on overseas trade. While it could supply cotton pieces to the Indian peasant and railways to the Argentine without serious competition from anybody else the bargain seemed to most men to be fair enough. It gave a remarkably good living to a few people, a high standard of comfort to a good many, and the means to maintain the small decencies of life to the great mass of folk in factory and office. Agriculture eventually suffered and the land went back to waste partly because grain could be bought far more cheaply abroad when the great American Middle West was opened up; but, to be fair, also partly because the farmer was a man of fixed habit who, if he could not grow corn at a profit, would face ruin rather than produce the milk and eggs and vegetables that could find so ready and so uncompetitive a market in the towns of Britain. Two world wars fought for thinly disguised commercial motives, the loss of credit balances abroad, and the fact that British industry has been equalled and overtaken in efficiency, initiative, craftsmanship, and salesmanship by many other countries, have closed to us the markets of which we were once in arrogant, undisputed possession; and the sands upon which the national prosperity was founded in 1846 stand revealed with their instability patent for all to see.

The second point, which may at the moment be merely repeated so that it shall not be forgotten, was that enunciated by Malthus and seized upon by the Cobdenites: that the growing of food upon the inherently infertile soils of these islands is a practice which is indefensible by any of the tenets of the classical economists. There is today much talk again of these marginal areas, and much sentimentality poured out upon the virtues of reclaiming the uplands and preserving their native populations as the nurseries of the sound pioneering blood of old England. The romanticist looks, with the Psalmist, up into the hills and sees there the nation's strength. But even Cobbett, with his violent partisanship of agriculture, looked at the hills south-east of Winchester in

1823 and saw that the Napoleonic reclamation had overshot itself. 'These hills are among the most barren in England; yet a part of them was broken up during the rage for improvements. A man must be mad, or nearly mad, to sow wheat upon such a spot.' Any decision on whether it is wise to invest the nation's money in these marginal lands—in the form of subsidies or of commodity prices fixed high enough to recompense the upland farmer for his low level of production—must be based upon an assessment of the nation's need to live upon her own resources and the price she can afford to pay for a high or complete degree of self-sufficiency. In the circumstances of the closing decades of the nineteenth century and the first years of the twentieth the involuntary decision to let these hills go out of use was perhaps an inevitable one: the land does not die, but goes into a sleep from which the fairy prince of a booming market can fairly quickly awaken it.

All through the century from 1770 to 1870, with the exception of the Napoleonic War years, there were loud and continuous complaints by the corn-growers of ruinous prices. The fall from the Napoleonic blockade peak of 126s. 6d. in 1812 to 38s. 6d. in 1851 was certainly a spectacular one, but more so from the height of the peak to which prices had soared rather than from the depths of the abyss into which they fell, and from the disproportionate rise in other farm returns and outlays than from any great loss upon the wheat crop itself. In the eighty years from 1770 to 1850, for instance, the rent of arable land doubled, or so Caird calculated; wages rose by one-third; and while butter, meat, and wool prices almost or completely doubled, apart from much greater production per acre, wheat had regained the same, or a slightly lower, figure in 1850 as that at which it had stood in 1770. The corn-grower had a legitimate complaint against his landlord, who was charging him a rent of £2 an acre for arable land off which he took no more value in wheat than he had when it had stood at £1 before Buonaparte set Europe aflame. The fluent and influential pen of Philo-Agricolae wrote in the *Mark Lane Express* in 1835 that 'it is utterly impossible for the most skilful farmer in Christendom to till without incurring an absolute and positive loss, nay though he unite in his own application the experience of a Tusser and a Bakewell, a Tull and a Young. Let the land-lords adopt corn rents and share with their tenants the calamity of low markets and the advantages of high ones.' Not only was the farmer's complaint a legitimate one, but the class against which it was directed had much to answer for.

The great rural landlords of the eighteenth and nineteenth centuries proved to the hilt the old dictum that property is power; and as Burke remarked, the Houses of Lords and Commons were their first lines of defence of their hereditary estates. Although it might breed a few effeminate coxcombs, the upper class of landlords possessed a physical toughness that sprang from long days in the saddle and remained little harmed by long nights at or under the table, and the mental fibre to discard all but the eldest male kitten in the litter. But when they had to dower their daughters they could often only do it by raising money by a mortgage charge upon their lands which in the nature of events they had little hope of ever being able to redeem. The amount of entailed land that was encumbered with debt up to the hilt has never been computed; but it was probably the greater part of the countryside.

Their financial embarrassments prevented many landlords from fulfilling their functions in a still predominantly agri-cultural society: as beneficent overseers of the tenants' use of their land; as the founts of farming wisdom; as the sources of improving and furnishing the land for good husbandry; and, perhaps above all, as the buffers between the world and the farmer, the springs which took the main force of the impact of bad times upon the agrarian economy. And, it must be said, where the means were present the will to use them to fulfil the duties of a landed proprietor—the corollary of the rights—was absent. John Stuart Mill, who was so wrong in so much of what he said, was right when he held that non-cultivating owners could only justify their ownership by being improvers. Whatever may be the case with other forms of property, the justification of ownership of land is a functional, paternal, unselfish and assiduous attention to the health and wise use of that land. It is a high task, nothing less than the custody of the universal source of life; but only a few men had both the desire and the ability to essay it.

When farming was somewhat in the fashion among the great men of Britain in the eighteenth and early nineteenth centuries the examples of good husbandry which they set were of immense value to the progress of agriculture. The work of Coke and Townshend, to mention the best-known if not intrinsically the best, was copied right down the social scale on estates here and there in Britain. The fashion, however, never became universal; nor was it entirely altruistic, for even Coke made a handsome profit from the sale of livestock at the Clippings which he held for the good of agriculture. The tradition of good landlordship on even the limited scale that it reached dwindled gradually, however, and when Caird toured England in 1850 and 1851 his reports made shameful reading. It is unlikely that he was unjust to the landed gentry, for he was reporting for *The Times*, which under Delane's editorship reflected rather than led public opinion; and when he could say anything good of an English landlord he made a point of doing so. There was, for instance, the Duke of Portland, whose introduction of a 'corn rent' was followed on the better run estates. It was essentially a sliding scale of rent tied to the price of corn, with no lower limit but a reasonable upper one. On Lord Spencer's estate 'good landlords are hereditary', some of the farms had been held by the same families for 300 years, the average length of tenancy was ninety years; and all without any written agreement. Spencer's agent visited every field during the year to give advice on its management. Large sums had been spent on new buildings, drainage, the amendment of farm boundaries and on seventy-four labourers' cottages. Lord Beverley on his Airmyn estate was solicitous of the welfare of the workers on his tenants' farms and provided each of them with a good house, a garden, a cowgate of an acre and a half of the best pasture and the same area of meadow for hay, and the benefit of a cow club to recompense them if their stock died. The pick of the landlords were among the great aristocrats; but there was another section of society which managed its estates with wisdom and benevolence. Some of the best landlords were the capitalists from the towns who gave their lands the same attention to detail as that which had gained them their success in business, and the same care for honest dealing as that which gave Britain her reputation for integrity. The same tradition of sound land management still lingers in this class, by no means universally but far more widely than the many critics of the business-man-become-farmer admit.

That was the pleasant, commendable side of the picture; to which may be added William Wells' immensely successful reclamation of that last outpost of the watery Fens, Whittlesey Mere, and the work of the ironfounder family of Knights in attempting to tame the wilderness of Exmoor. Both were examples of how the wealth, enterprise, and patriotism of enlightened landlordism could work for the benefit of Britain. The reverse side was a blot upon the face of Victorian rural society. A handful of quotations from the pages of Caird will illustrate it. The Duke of Marlborough had put up his rents by a third ten years before Caird went to see him, with no accompanying improvements, and he refused any abatement in bad times. There was no confidence between landlord and tenant, and the Blenheim countryside looked poverty-stricken and neglected. The livelihood of the tenants of the Marquess of Exeter was completely eaten up by the game which his lordship preserved for his amusement, and against whose depredations upon the crops 'no man can farm'; and Caird omitted to tell his readers that the Marquess also insisted upon the retention of the open fields of Stamford so that his patronage of the Parliamentary seat might continue undisputed. The general run of landlords of Oxfordshire, of Devon, of Wiltshire, of Essex—indeed, of almost every county—took no interest in agriculture, and employed as agents town solicitors who knew nothing of farming, but much of how to screw rents out of tenants whose holdings were in the last stages of decay. The early Victorian period, in fact, saw the rise of a rich, leisured class with no occupation except the pursuit of pleasure and no contact with the new science of husbandry. It had not even the excuse of the patronage of an art which was worth the name. The class persisted, widely admired, for a century; but it has now virtually disappeared.

Caird found that the landlords everywhere took, in increased rents, their full share of the returns from the progress of agriculture, from the rising markets for produce, from the accumulating riches of the country. The good ones helped their tenants in bad times by granting them rent rebates. The bad ones were such as those in the Fens who made no reduction in rent on account of low prices; and in one case where the tenantry made representation to their landlord to this end the only reply was a notice to quit to the man whose name stood first on the petition. Nine landlords out of ten took no steps to replace the inconvenient, ill-arranged hovels of farm buildings, which were 'devoid of every improvement for economizing labour, food and manure, which are a reproach to the landlords'. The cry of Crawley came down over the centuries, but went unheeded and unheard: 'If the possessioners would consider themselves to be but stewards . . .' The worse type is seen in its irascible public performances in some of Trollope's squires and in the pages of Jane Austen and the Brontës.

Scottish agricultural improvement, initiated and largely carried through by the great rural landlords, followed in part the English pattern; and in the process it earned the Highland chieftain in particular the obloquy of succeeding generations of social philosophers, but it is certain that he did not deserve the full measure at least of the odium cast upon him. His task of modernizing and rationalizing the farming on his estates was infinitely more difficult than that of his English counterpart because there was far more leeway to be made up. It would have been difficult (as Mr. James Handley says in his recent and distinguished *Scottish Farming in the Eighteenth Century*) to find a territory of equal area in the inhabited Europe of the time that offered so much of poverty, misery, and barrenness as did Scotland before Culloden. Fletcher of Saltoun wrote in 1698 that one in every five or six of its people lived upon the verge of utter destitution. Hardly any money circulated in the country; and the presence of an elephant in their midst, said General Wade's revenue agent, Burt, would hardly cause more surprise among the natives than the sight of a spoked wheel. The agriculture of most of the lowlands was poor; and in the Highlands weeds overtopped the crops of oats in the little arable plots and, 'taking one year with another the quantity of weed seeds must be nearly equal to that of the grain produced'. The natural sloth of the Highlander in his own land, gross overstocking of the hills with cattle, the cessation of the natural controls upon population which followed the abolition of clan warfare and the introduction of vaccination against smallpox, all meant that as the eighteenth century progressed much of upland and inland Scotland had very many more folk than it could maintain in decency and even a low degree of prosperity. The result was the picture Pennant drew: 'A set of people worn down with poverty; their habitation scenes of misery, made of loose stones; without chimneys, without doors . . . the furniture perfectly corresponds . . . the pot filled with fare that may rather be called a permission to exist than a support of a vigorous life.' The potato came into general cultivation here in the middle of the eighteenth century, but served only to encourage and permit the breeding of more children, with the inevitable greater disaster when the crop failed.

Enclosure of the ancient runrig fields proceeded steadily in the lowlands from the beginning of the century, with some dispossession of the small peasantry in favour of the 'professional' farmers of the new, larger enclosed holdings. The process was made the easier by the fact that both here and in the Highlands, where the aggregation of the ancient tiny crofts into sheep runs followed, there were only a few score of landlords in any county. There was often immense misery of mind as a result of the Highland 'clearances', when the crofters of the clans voluntarily left or were ejected from their ancestral glens; but their material condition could hardly have been worsened in the process, and emigration sent many of them to find comfort and fortune and freedom overseas. The result of this remarkable, rapid, ruthless but certainly necessary agrarian revolution, achieved by individual effort of the landlord and with the encouragement and tuition of the Highland Society was, in the words of the *Scottish Farmer*, to 'free Scotland from the thraldom of old customs and ideas, to transform its barren heaths into smiling cornfields, rich pastures and tree-clad slopes, to turn its ill-fed and ill-bred livestock into breeds with a world-wide fame for excellence, to combat animal and plant diseases and pests, to promote the art of craftsmanship in agriculture and rural industries, and to uplift the way of life of the people'.

Nowhere else in the Old World had the land come to be farmed so much on a money basis as in Britain. How much of the profitability of British farming in the century from 1770 to 1870 was due to the cheap labour with which farm produce was grown is a moot point. It is certain, however, that the man at the plough handle, with the flail in the barn, tending the livestock, reached the nadir of degradation during these years. Starved himself, he watched his family eke out an existence that was no better than that of the Egyptian *fellahin* of today. The wonder was that the rural labourer as a whole maintained his integrity and self-respect to the extent that he did. National affairs worked against him on every hand. Enclosure had swept away his little anchor of independence in the commons; and the shift from domestic industry to factory production had robbed his family of their chance to supplement his small earnings. As late as 1851 Caird found the village inhabitants of Wiltshire were 'principally a decayed manufacturing population, among whom handloom weaving and pillow lace working still keep a languid existence'. But where the rural industries survived, as among the class of weaver-smallholders in the West Riding with looms in their homes, the people could ring the changes between the profits of the loom and the land. And the same is still true today of the miner-smallholders who live on the hillsides above the valleys of Glamorgan.

But where the domestic industries had gone, society, jealous in the plenitude of its private possessions, persecuted the labourer when he sought to continue to find his fuel in the hedgerows as his ancestors had done for innumerable centuries; and it put a stop to the custom of gleaning, a custom so immemorially ancient that those who thought it a right had a rude awakening when the Court of Common Pleas, deciding against the gleaners, contradicted the letter of the Mosaic law that the gleanings should be left 'unto the poor, and to the stranger'. Industrial agriculture could no longer be bothered to sell the labourer's wife a pint or two of milk a day or a bushel of wheat now and again; and the family was thrown upon the mercies of the village shopkeeper. And the labourer was unable to escape from his local miseries and seek to better himself in the great world outside his parish boundary. The Carolian poor law prohibited all who might conceivably stand in need of parochial relief from moving from their birthplaces except under rigid and rarely conceded conditions. This had not mattered so much when the labourer was a little landed man who could find some sort of a livelihood upon his few acres or by the exercise of his common rights. But when these precarious insurances against utter penury had left him, he lay completely at the mercy of a handful of employers and in a surfeited labour market. Medicine was increasing his kind; the progress of agricultural mechanization was decreasing his opportunities of employment; and his freedom to find his fortune outside agriculture was usually statute-barred.

His masters the farmers and their masters the landlord, faced across the Channel with a terrifying example of what a peasantry out of control could do and realizing that the 'poor in a loomp is bad', sought many remedies for rural distress; all, in fact, except the right one of giving Hodge a fairer share of the profits of his work. The fear was, and it was probably well founded, that while wages could be raised in a period of prosperity, they could not so easily be reduced when prosperity came to an end. An alternative had to be found, therefore, if seigneurial blood was to be kept from staining the cobbles of market-places in England as it had done in France. The rapidly rising cost of living of the period of the Napoleonic Wars had to be offset by reducing the standard of living of the underpaid farm labourer, or by supplementing his income temporarily and indirectly. An attempt to make the labourer abandon the wheaten bread which had only recently come into use among the working classes failed because the labourer had 'lost his rye teeth' and he regarded the maslin loaf as a sign of loss of what little rags of respectability still clung to him. A proposal in 1795 to introduce a minimum wage offended the tenets of economic freedom which were so affectionately held. A policy of equipping the labourer with a little land, with the produce from which he could supplement his wages, was as nearly stillborn as made no matter; but where it was tried it was a remarkable success, for it took Hodge out of complete dependence upon his cash income and returned to him something of his old self-respect. In this last way 'public charity began to give to the labourer what public justice should never have permitted him as a freeman to lose'.

When society did at last find a solution to the problem of the underpaid and starving farm labourer it was one which was typical of contemporary thought. He and his whole class were, with a few small exceptions in northern parishes, sold to the poor law. The plan evolved by the Berkshire justices sitting in assembly at the Pelican Inn at Speenhamland fixed a basic requirement for a labourer and his family tied to the price of bread, and made up any deficiency between his earned wage and his estimated need out of the rates. The farm labourer became a pauper even when he was in full employment, and for nearly half a century he suffered all the degradations of pauperdom, receiving the bulk of his income from the parish overseer, living in many places in the hovels that so offended the eye of Cobbett— 'their dwellings are little better than pig beds'—clad in rags, barely nourished upon bread and cheese and water, and without hope for the future. Caird described how he often had to live. The valley village of Wark in Northumberland was 'the very picture of slovenliness and neglect. Wretched houses piled here and there without order, filth of every kind scattered about or heaped up against the walls; horses, cows and pigs lodged under the same roof with their owners and entering by the same door.' This was the rural England of the early nineteenth century, to which the romanticist turns for his rosy-faced ploughman, the laughing little country girl, the neat cottage wife beneath the honeysuckled door. What laughter and neatness and health there were in the country-side at this time were a triumph of suffering mankind over its circumstances.

Even setting aside the occasional tendentiousness of the Hammonds' *Village Labourer*—and there is little evidence that much of their terrible picture is overdrawn—the facts which are set out in the parliamentary and other committee reports of the time are an indictment of the whole society of the period; and an indelible blot upon the religion to which landlord, tenant, and servile parson all paid lip-service, a religion founded upon precepts of universal brotherhood, but which was mangled into a justification of degree, priority, and place. Starving boys, escaping death from spring guns, found themselves in prison for poaching at an age when they could not even dress themselves; and the fathers of decent English families, transported after affrays with the gamekeepers, murdered each other by mutual pact in order to escape from the hell of Botany Bay. They had not even got the Church on their side. The bench of bishops were the brothers in repression of the most intolerant of the landlords; and their clergy were the domestic chaplains of the squirearchy and allied with them against the village poor. There were exceptions, but they were few. The largest cargo of human suffering to reach Australia from the homely English country-side was that of the 457 men and boys transported for their part in the well-disciplined but abortive riots of 1830. They were sentenced for their destruction of the threshing machines that were depriving them of their winter work with flails in the barns, and the burning of the ricks of such gentlemen as he who was heard to remark of the poor: 'Ah, I should be well pleased if a plague were to break out among them, and then I should have their carcases as manure, and right good stuff it would make for my hops.' The condition of rural Britain in the early nineteenth century gave the lie direct to those academic economists who, half a century before, had been preaching the doctrine that, by taking the land from the cottager, that cottager must become a useful member of society by being forced to enter full agricultural employment.

In the event, the farmer did not benefit from the Speenhamland system any more than did the labourer, for under it the burden of the poor rate became oppressive; and particularly so upon the smaller farmer, who employed few or no men, but still had to contribute through the poor rate to the maintenance of the men working for his larger neighbours. The Report on the Poor Laws of 1834 said that 'the overseer has sometimes called upon little farmers for their rates and found that they had no provision of any kind in the house nor money to buy any'. Speenhamland also aggravated the habit of destroying cottages in one parish, thus reducing the number of the poor to be maintained within the village, and employing for casual work men from neighbouring parishes, who, when out of employment, became a charge upon their own ratepayers. The result was that in closed parishes where the cottages were destroyed the labourers had to come many miles to work. In the Lincolnshire wolds they travelled several miles each way on donkeys.

The roots of the labour troubles of this and previous periods were the over-population of rural England and the periodicity of agricultural work. The first problem has now completely disappeared. The second is fast disappearing with the levelling effect of mechanization upon the farm labour needs through the year. But when corn growing was at its peak in this century from 1770 to 1870, the seasonal demands for workers were immensely variable; and the depth of the poverty of the rural poor during the same period is no coincidence. Hudson of Castle Acre, on the Holkham estate, harvested his 600 acres of cereals with 96 workers: 32 mowers, 32 to gather the cut crop, and 32 to bind the sheaves; and many of these hands were thrown out of work after harvest with no land of their own to fall back upon for their sustenance. The Committee on Agriculture of 1833 reported, in fact, that there were few surplus labourers during the summer, but unemployment began very soon after harvest and remained until the spring. The first threshing machines, which were the objects of the fury of the rural workers in the 1830 riots, made the trouble worse, for a farm labourer could no longer count on flailing to give him a quarter of his whole year's work. One of the results of the seasonality of farm work was the demoralizing gang system which flourished particularly in the arable areas of East Anglia from the 1820's, and in which men, women, and young children were organized into roving working parties under a gang-master, sleeping rough and promiscuously. With the father's wages at starvation level, children were placed by their parents in gang or other labour in order to earn a few more pence for the family budget. The much-vaunted cleanliness of English arable crops during the period of high Victorian farming was the result of tens of thousands of small fingers roughened and small backs bent for ever over the endless business of hand-weeding the corn. Caird noted of a Suffolk farm that 'after hoeing the wheat is gone over by children and every weed picked off. When it is reaped it is forked over by men and every patch of twitch removed.' Not until the Education Act of 1876 were the infants of the countryside taken from the cold, wet fields into the village classroom; and even then the change was not all gain, for in the rural schools small boys and girls were taught the lessons and the outlook of urban Britain.

The sociologists who saw that the divorce of the bulk of British men from the ownership or tenancy of land was at the root of the poverty of the time also dimly realized that it was impossible, and indeed not perhaps desirable, to put the hands of the clock back to the high noon of peasant farming. It seemed to them, however, that the squalor and degradation of rural Britain might be amended by giving the farm labourer a few rods of land of his own again, so that the twilight, if not the full sunshine, of independence might return to him. For long, however, far too few people accepted this premise for any action to be taken upon it. The allotment movement progressed slowly, partly from public apathy; partly from the suspicion of the beneficiaries who saw in it yet another weapon to beat down their wages; but mainly from the opposition of the farmers, who had no reason to want their workmen to become less dependent, who feared that they would expend all their energies on their own plots, and who were too jealous of their acres to set any apart for a rural betterment in which they did not believe and which many of them in their hearts did not want to see.

But while there were many men who were jealously guarding every British acre which could be brought into their possession, and even more men desiring to be employed thereon, the colonies could show their wide virgin lands ripe for the taking. Colonial territories were attractive not only to small farmers and farm workers who found their little territorial ambitions thwarted at home, but also to the urban workmen who sought to change their industrial slavery for the freedom of the pioneer. The Potters' Union, for instance, bought 12,000 acres in the western states of America and re-sold them to its members for a payment of 6*d.* a week. In the first three decades of the reign of Victoria more than 5 million people of these islands went overseas to seek their fortunes, three-quarters of them in the United States and the rest in Canada, Australia, and New Zealand. Many of them were Irishmen, driven out by the very potato famines which, by forcing the corn law repeal issue to a head, laid the foundations of their own colonial prosperity and the ruin of the landlords and the masters whom they left behind them. Those who survived the two-months-long Atlantic crossing in disease-ridden, filthy, and overcrowded sailing ships which could be smelt at extreme gunshot range, found themselves in a primitive land, but one in which hard work and a measure of good luck had their reward. Australia and New Zealand were slowly converted from convict stations for the 75,000 unwanted souls transported there in the half-century after 1788 into lands where enterprise and a concentration upon money-making could build a fortune. Some of the ex-convicts themselves prospered. Even the younger landless sons of great British families found there a pleasant and profitable combination of life on horseback, free land, and a rising industry of sheep-ranching with the merinos that grew the fine wool that English flockmasters had abandoned for Bakewell's meaty, coarse-fleeced masterpieces of the breeder's art. It was a combination that was vastly attractive to a man who wanted fresh air and money and could live without the civilities and the arts of his homeland. In South Africa an unmarried English farm labourer who had earned less than £1 a month at home could make his £6 a month and his keep, and save fast enough to become a farmer in his own right very quickly.

However much may be deplored the sentiment which makes the English village of one or two centuries ago a microcosm of Elysium, the fact still remains, however, that behind the poverty, the incest of many-peopled bedrooms, the damp mud floors and streaming walls, the hatreds which burnt ricks and shot gamekeepers, behind these evil things there still lay the shreds of the unity of an ancient community that was living sufficiently of itself and close enough to the essence of things to enjoy the intangible inner harmony which was denied to the man who trod the pavements of the town. The village had the remnants of the incredibly old rites of Mayday and harvest home, Yuletide and the fertility ceremonies of Easter to stand as silent and now incomprehensible witness of its remote origins; the relics of the old agrarian disciplines which had turned Britain from a wilderness into a vast, fertile garden; the vestiges of a neighbourliness which loved mankind because it knew its origins, its virtues and its vices so very well; and it had the sunshine and the clear sky, the scent of cottage flowers and beanfields, of hay in the making and the clean rawness of newly ploughed earth. When the villager went to the town to live and work he had none of these things. His wages might be higher and more secure, his home drier, the streets paved, and gin to be had at a halfpenny the tot. But in place of the neighbourliness there was only the cold unconcern of strangers too unhappy to be kind; in place of the hay and the flowers only putrid unburied corpses and the stagnant street water polluted with the faeces of an undrained slum; in place of the old rural self-respect which had survived so many tribulations an emptiness which found relief only in blind drunkenness or the intoxication of revivalism; and in place of the indigenous culture a vicarious, unsatisfying sampling of life at second hand at the penny readings, touching Nature only through the remote removes of print instead of direct by hand and eye.

On the land these labourers were leaving because it would not pay them a living wage, the profits from farming in the piping times of war were very high; and the general doubling of rents in the period of the Napoleonic Wars gave the land-owners their full share of them. The great majority of the landlords continued to take the same revenue out of their estates right up to the collapse of British arable farming in the 1870's; and they could always let their farms with ease, and often to hand-picked tenants. The reason was not far to seek. Farming remained, even in the comparative slumps of the third decade of the nineteenth century, a profitable occupation when it was efficiently pursued; and even the relatively inefficient husbandman could count, over a period of years, on maintaining his family in some degree of comfort. Efficiency, however, was becoming the touchstone of success or failure in farming. The days in which a man who could feed his family from the produce of his acres counted himself secure against the world had gone. Agricultural efficiency, of course, can be defined in many ways: as the highest possible production of food from a given area of land; as the conservation and gradual increase of the fertility of a holding; as taking a high profit from the capital invested, which in its turn may mean either intensive or extensive farming; or in self-sufficient farming, producing food with little or no call upon outside resources, which is the current aim. A man's success in one or more of these manifestations of efficiency depended upon several mental and material attributes: a knowledge of the craft and mystery of the traditional art of husbandry—which, with all due deference to the wiseacres of all centuries, is far from being the most difficult of the mental attributes to acquire; a sympathetic interest in new ideas and the flair to accept the good ones and discard the bad; enough capital to finance the operations of the farm; a receptiveness of agricultural instruction; and the external influences of the state, international commerce, and the price of equipment and raw material for the farm.

These last were probably the most important of the factors which now controlled the profit or loss of the farming year. The state, above all, was playing an increasing part in the world of agriculture. The opening or closing of the ports of Britain to foreign grain and livestock regulated to a very great extent the internal prices of cereals and meat, and could make all the difference between bankruptcy and affluence. The farmer was also losing his self-sufficiency in the tools and raw materials of his industry. Life was once uncomplicated. The dung came from the stock-yard or the sheep-fold; the plough and seedlip and scythe from the village blacksmith and carpenter; the cereal seed from the farm itself or by exchange with a neighbour; the grass seeds for pasture or meadow from the sweepings of the hay barn; and the farm buildings were made from the timber of the local woods and the bricks of the local brickyard. As the nineteenth century progressed all this was changed, not in the twinkling of an eye, but slowly and intermittently. Fertility now proceeded from the accumulated droppings of generations of South American sea-birds, dried and bagged and shipped to Britain; from the bones of the slaughter-yards, the battlefield of Waterloo, the charnel houses of the Continent, all dissolved by Lawes' new process into super-phosphate; and from the potash mines of Germany and the phosphatic rocks of Africa. In many spheres of fertility, Britain borrowed and pursued the fundamental work of German scientists, as earlier generations had taken up the threads of a new agriculture and livestock husbandry where the Dutch had left off. Cattle were still fed partly upon the barley and oats, beans and peas of British fields, but increasingly also upon processed, concentrated foods in cake or meal form which came to these islands bearing within themselves the fertility of foreign fields and leaving behind them at home the accumulating deficiencies in soil structure which led to world-wide erosion. Through these imported concentrated feeds even the dung that passed from the stock in the yards of Norfolk, in the stalls and cowsheds of the Home Counties, in the pastures of the Vale of Aylesbury was bestowing upon British clays and loams and sands the goodness of the arable lands of the American Mid-west and the cotton silts of the lower Nile.

The early and mid-Victorian farmer was also becoming more dependent upon the agricultural machinery manu-facturer for the tools of his trade. His plough bodies were ceasing to be made by a hedge carpenter and the coulters and shares by the village blacksmith to designs which had not changed very much for several centuries; instead, he bought from the great Ipswich firm of Ransomes a scientifically designed cast-iron plough, with half the draught and twice the efficiency of his old wooden ones. The simple wooden seedlip gave place to a seed drill, elaborated by Smyth of Peasenhall from the ideas of Tull. The corn harvest was cut not by an army of scythes-men, but by one of the new reapers of Parson Bell or Cyrus McCormick. The flail and the winnowing in the wind were being superseded by one of the new horse-driven threshing machines that were being made by many local firms. The steam engine was beginning to replace man and horse and oxen as the motive force on the farm. And the new materials of agriculture, the seeds of wheat and the other cereals, of clovers and the other constituents of the grass field, were being empirically selected and sold to him by Mr. Thomas Gibbs, seedsman to the Board of Agriculture, who could provide from his establishment at the corner of Half Moon Street everything from Russian hemp to honeysuckle, the new mangel-wurzels, fourteen kinds of turnip and no fewer than twenty-six varieties of vetch.

The livestock farmer—and the time had not yet come when men farmed without stock—also had new tools to his hand, new and potentially more profitable raw material to be worked up into beef and mutton, wool and milk. The improvement of the animals of the farm had proceeded silently through the centuries until the combination of the work of Bakewell, the Collings and their fellows, and of the agricultural journalists—Young and Marshall, Culley and Lawrence, who wrote so lengthily of their results—awoke some men to a realization that here were the means by which the insatiable urban demand for red meat could be very profitably met. Both the beast and the sheep that took an unconscionable time to flesh were being replaced by Bakewell's new Leicesters, the hybrid Shorthorns of the Collings, the square perambulating joints of prime mutton that came from the Southdown flocks of Webb of Babraham, and the incomparable beef of the Devons of the Quartleys and of the Aberdeen-Angus of M'Combie.

These were the new instruments of arable and pastoral husbandry that were coming to the hand of the British farmer in the first half of the nineteenth century—the implements that could work faster and more cheaply than Hodge; the livestock that paid a greater and a quicker dividend on the food invested in its rearing and fattening; and new fertilizers to supplement, and later often to replace, the dung that was and still is considered to be the mainspring of fertility. All these were the result of the adolescent science which at last was finally shaking off the shackles of Aristotle and the alchemists which had lain for so long on the theory and practice of British farming. But how to spread the news of them and the knowledge of how to use them? This is a problem that is as old as agriculture itself; and its solution has become a matter of growing urgency as an increasing number of non-producers have become more and more dependent on a decreasing number of producers for their food; and a matter of supreme importance to the producers themselves as the reliance upon external sources for their materials and an external market for their produce has brought with it a nicer margin between the costs of production and the selling price. The education of the men to whose keeping the land is entrusted for the benefit of society is obviously a matter of fundamental importance, both to the society whose interest it is that it shall be well used and to the trustees whose livelihood it is. The problem was complicated in the past by the fact that farming was the most conservative of all callings, many members of which were content to hold by the ancient mysteries of their craft and to ignore the valid findings of inquisitive, imaginative, and venturesome men. A proper scepticism of unproved theories is a quality necessary in any stable society; but a sceptic with his ears and eyes tightly closed makes a static state. Caird told the story of the farmer who, coming from a 'two-horse country', continued to use a two-horse plough on his new farm for thirty years, ploughing an acre a day with it. And yet his neighbours, reared in the tradition that demanded six or eight horses to the plough team, still insisted that it was quite impossible to plough their land with only two horses. This is a rural attitude to life for the virtual disappearance of which in the present generation society may give thanks; but it was an attitude against which the improvers of the past came to a full stop. By the middle of the nineteenth century the only valid excuse for it—that the transport of men and ideas was so difficult in the absence of railways, good roads, and a sound popular agricultural Press—was fast disappearing. Hitherto the art of husbandry in any one county had been a closed book to the men of the next, except in so far as the rural gentry of the two met and mixed in Parliament or in metropolitan drawing-rooms.

The importance of breaking down the ancient barriers to a new farming—barriers of a lack of desire as often as a lack of opportunity to learn—had been appreciated by a handful of the more imaginative of the agrarian preceptors for many centuries. Walter of Henley had put his ideas down on parchment for the benefit of his fellows and not for his own magnification, as the best of his successors down the years had done—Fitzherbert the surveyor, Tusser the farmer-poet, Blith the Roundhead Cincinnatus, and Bradley the professor of botany. The best of the landlords, the Carolian Royal Society and a host of more or less informed pamphleteers had also essayed the task of agricultural education before the closing years of the eighteenth century. Then, in the atmosphere of intellectual intoxication which both followed and caused the Industrial Revolution, minds devoted to the

commendable task of agricultural progress indulged themselves in the fashionable pursuit of combination for the betterment of society. They founded farm discussion associations,
agricultural improvement associations, and, as a culmination, a Board of Agriculture which was honoured by the first
government grant of money ever made for the improvement
of British farming. It was preceded and followed by the
foundation of the great societies—the Bath and West of
England, the Royal, the Royal Highland and Agricultural—
dedicated not only to the achievement of higher national
standards in arable and livestock husbandry, but also to the
betterment of rural living in all its aspects. It is a pity that
some of them have now come to have as their sole objects
the organization of agricultural shows. The spate of surveys
and essays, inquiries and experiments met a response from
the small, receptive section of the agricultural community;
but the hard core of the unresponsive remained—and
remains, although now shrunk to far less disturbing proportions. The major aim of all this work in its many guises was
the simple one of stimulating the agricultural mind to
inquire, to look about, note and ponder what it saw, to
experiment, and to read. Bakewell, the livestock genius,
expressed it as an injunction to take out the nag and see what
other people were doing; Young, the inspired journalist
secretary of the Board of Agriculture, gave advice to every
farmer to spend his winter evenings entering in his commonplace book 'queries, speculations, calculations' of how best
to do this work or that, together with all 'inquiries, doubts
or prepositions' worth recording.

But this was pre-eminently a period in which the results
of the insatiable curiosity of the few were coming far faster
than they could be absorbed by the many, for the private
dissemination of farming knowledge could only be a hit-and-
miss affair at the best; the most that the ancient seats of learning had yet achieved was the foundation of the ill-endowed

chairs at Edinburgh and Oxford; and the Royal Agricultural College at Cirencester, excellent institution though it was, was designed to further the education of squire and agent rather than that of the working farmer. In vain did the Italian razor-strop-maker who turned farmer, John Joseph Mechi, declaim that 'we want an agricultural college in every county'.

The ultimate rural obstacles to the spread of new ideas and practices, however, were some degree of inflexibility in the general agricultural mind and a somewhat higher degree of inflexibility in both the material and economic structure of British farming. The rural mind, accustomed to the slow changes of the seasons and the social machine, was also very understandably unable to keep pace with the rapid disintegration of economic stability which was a corollary of the nation's new emphasis upon industry and commerce as the bulwarks of national prosperity. The more enlightened of the commentators on rural enterprises too often beat their heads against a brick wall, which was not all of the farmer's own building, when they pointed to the roads along which the arable and livestock man might most comfortably travel to keep abreast of the times. Corn-growing, for instance, had been immensely stimulated by the high prices of the Napoleonic Wars. The arable farmers—and in the piping days all men ploughed up all the acres they could for wheat—were reluctant to believe that the era of inflated prices was over, and continued to produce bread corn at a level which deprived it of its scarcity value. The stubborn adherence to cereal-growing persisted for a very long time, although, in fact, for a decade or two before the collapse of the 1870's it paid well again because the demands of the population were overtaking the combined supplies of home and overseas producers.

There were, however, new horizons opening up in the sky for the British farmer; and if he had heeded, and been able to heed, the long-sighted prophets he might have saved his children ruin in the years to come. Of the population in 1851 one-half now lived in the towns in sufficient prosperity to be able to discard the loaf as the principal item in its diet and to substitute a very great deal of meat and butter, milk and fresh vegetables. It was estimated that a 'gentleman's family' spent only £1 2s. 4d. a head a year on bread, but £9 10s. on meat, butter, and milk. The same change in balance in the national diet operated all down the urban scale. The result was that wheat in this year was giving much the same cash return per acre as it had done in the 1770's, although wages had risen by nearly a half and rents were more than doubled. But on the other hand, where a farm had produced £100 worth of meat and dairy produce in 1770 it could now turn out £200 from the same area and with no improvement of stock or land taken into account. Improved breeds of cattle and sheep and improving methods of management of grass, to say nothing of the advent of cheap imported feeding-stuffs, could double or treble this figure. The weight of beast coming into Smithfield in 1710 at five or six years old was about 370 lb., but in 1795 it had become 800 lb. In 1842 William Mason showed at the Smithfield Club's show a Shorthorn ox with a dead weight of 2,117 lb. at four years ten months, and there were many others nearly as meaty. It had cost its breeder very little more to rear and fatten than the runts of 1710, but it brought a profit many-fold greater. The new opportunities in meat were not widely taken, although Caird was warning his readers that 'with the extension of railways and steam navigation there seems good reason to anticipate the permanence of a low range of prices for corn. The safe course for the English agriculturist is to endeavour by increasing his stock to render himself less dependent on corn.' In 1832 between 2,000 and 3,500 beast were coming into the great Smithfield Market every week, tramping Londonwards along the dusty roads. The yard-fed polls from East Anglia largely predominated in the spring, to be replaced later in the summer by the polled Scots, the Lincolnshire Shorthorns, the Welsh runts, and the Longhorns from the Leicestershire pastures that came in down the St. Albans road. Fifteen years later, and they were largely fifteen years of relatively unprofitable corn prices, the figures were nearly the same for beast from home sources, but they were beginning to be swollen by the trickle of German and Dutch bullocks that followed the repeal in 1843 of the ban on livestock imports. The trickle grew to a stream as European rearers stepped into the gap left wide open by British conservatism. The stream was to become a flood when the prairies and the new refrigerator ships combined to swamp the home market with American beef and New Zealand mutton.

The same opportunities were arising in the field of milk. In the past transport had been too slow to permit of this highly perishable commodity's being brought to town except from the immediate neighbourhood or in the form of butter and cheese. The railways were changing all that. Evening milk from the pastures of Cheshire or the Vale of the White Horse could be on the London doorsteps in the morning. Even so intelligent a man as Smith, the drainer of Deanston, did not foresee the results of the combination of the railways and the 'great mouth' gaping wide open for good milk. He told a Select Committee on the Railway Acts in 1846 that freight trains would be of inestimable value in moving stock from rearing grounds in the hills to the feeding pastures of the lowlands and thence to slaughteryard and market, and for taking the new chemical manures to the farm—as indeed they were; but he made no mention of milk. The great new opportunity was not grasped until the sheer necessity of the 1880's and 1890's forced the proud arable men to enter the ranks of the despised cow-keepers. It took very great adversity indeed to persuade men to make an end of the old song of the scythe and a beginning of the new song of the swish of milk in the pail.

The farmers' diffidence in making changes was, however, understandable, for they were often farming under conditions which made any alteration in their systems of husbandry both difficult and expensive, and sometimes impossible. In the first place, few of them had any real security of tenure. Leases for a term of years were the exception rather than the rule, and were in fact often declined by the tenant, for they might hamper a quick escape from depression. Occupation was from year to year. This, under a good landlord, was equivalent to tenure for life, or during the period of good behaviour, for even so great a tenant as George Hope of Fenton Barns was summarily ejected when his lease expired from the Lothian holding which he had made nearly as famous as Coke had made Holkham, for opposing the son of his landlord, Lord Wemyss, at the 1865 election. In almost all parts of the country there was no compensation for tenants' improvements, no tenant right. The result of these two factors, absence of tenurial security and lack of tenant right, made it a patently unwise step to incur expense in changing the mode of farming, or indeed to farm highly. Modern farm buildings were rarely met with; the existing buildings were inflexible units which could not readily be changed from cereal storage to livestock quarters; the landlord was often unwilling to incur the charge of re-equipping a holding to suit the whim of a tenant who might be gone tomorrow; and the tenant with little security was certainly not going to do it. A change in farming systems was also a highly expensive matter; and the capital often was not there. This question of the capital resources of agriculture was becoming one of importance, and it has grown more acute ever since.

Over and above all this there was in the earlier part of the period the depressive influence of tithe. This compulsory contribution of one-tenth of the produce of the land, and often to lay owners who could claim no spiritual right to the levy, but only a right of property, lay like a dead hand over all improvement. No other industry was subject to it; but the farmer who improved his stock or the yield of his crops was mulcted of the tithe of the profits of his improvements. Where tithe-ownership still lay in ecclesiastical hands it was opposed for reasons of denominational difference or of anti-clericalism. The collection of tithe in kind led to bitter feeling between parson and parishioner, particularly where a grasping cleric wrung one-tenth of the wage out of a starving labourer. In places a modus was arranged and tithes were commuted into a fixed cash payment. In 1836 they were universally commuted by statute in England and Wales, as they had been two centuries earlier in Scotland, and the tithe-owners south of the Scottish border received slightly over £4 million a year in lieu of the sheaves of corn and calves and lambs, milk and wool and fruit which had once flowed into their barns. The arrangement relieved the farmer of one of the major obstacles to the improvement of his agriculture and transferred the burden to his landlord; and it was in fact a not unsatisfactory arrangement while prices and rents were high. But when these fell the commuted tithe became a disproportionately high levy on the farm receipts.

In spite of all its mental and material faults, however, agriculture was serving the nation well. It was producing nearly all the grain the nation needed in 1851 and a large part of the meat. The 18 million people of England and Wales were being fed by the produce of $24\frac{1}{2}$ million acres of land, of which more than three-fifths were laid out in medium-sized holdings of between 100 and 500 acres and nearly another fifth in farms of more than 500 acres. Farming had become big business, a highly commercial venture like any other in Victorian Britain, but with this difference:

it suffered a chronic lack of financial backing because the commercial methods of joint stock financing were never applied to it. The farmer was left to manufacture wheat out of imported fertilizers and meat out of imported fodder with a monetary background which differed only in degree but not in nature from that against which the medieval peasant had practised his self-subsistent farming.

But above all the main characteristic of the period—indeed, of the whole era from the early Tudor renaissance in agriculture to the mid-Victorian heyday of the tenant farmer in his cornfields—was the schism between the land and the understanding of the mass of British people. The Industrial Revolution accelerated a process of detachment which is discernible far back in time. It ended in the land's becoming a closed book to five or six men in every ten, at least in so far as the realities of the great rural industry of food-growing were concerned. The urban reading public absorbed White's chronology of the birds and flowers of Selborne; it admired the detached beauties of the rural scene as interpreted by Cox and his school and by the brilliant touch of Bewick; and it stood amazed at the perception of Tennyson in noting the blackness of the buds of the ash tree. But all this was the sweeter aspect of the countryside, the gentlemanly matters which might be studied with propriety in the Victorian drawing-room or at the Victorian picnic. Apart from Crabbe, viewing the countryside in the tradition of Goldsmith and with a fierce indignation; apart from poor mad Clare, who came to write what he thought his readers would like to read anyway, and such dialect excursions into rural misfortune as Barnes' *Common a-Took In*; apart from these the country-side had no great man, artist or writer, to describe the miseries of the rural poor as Dickens had painted the sufferings of men and women and children in the towns. And mechanics was far too unfashionable a subject in polite society to permit the penning of a lyric of the reaper and the steam plough. It was all very artificial, and as the affairs of farming are restricted to the realities—and often the grosser realities—of life they could have no share in the nice culture of Victorian Britain. The chasm between field and factory was deepening fast; and the way was preparing for the great crash of British agriculture to fall upon unheeding, uninterested and antagonistic ears.

CHAPTER SEVEN

The World as Britain's Larder

IN THE era which began in the middle years of Victoria's
reign and ended with the outbreak of the First World
War the mass conscience of the nation was asleep when it
considered its land and the men who lived by and upon it.
And the lack of public regard for the supreme catalyst, the
brown earth which turns labour into a loaf of bread, had
as its immediate consequence the abdication of King Corn,
who had reigned for three centuries; and as its ultimate
result, perhaps, the dissolution of the old structure of landed
influence. The mantle of power which the ownership of acres
threw over the shoulders of the worthy and the unworthy
alike disintegrated in a very few decades. It had taken
many centuries to weave. And with it began to go the whole
complex network of rural society, a lace of infinitely varying
pattern, worked through more than 4,000 years, each part
linked to and dependent upon the others, and showing

157

through it at every point the background of green fields upon which it was supported. What is taking the place of this ancient web of life is not yet plain to see.

The period of little less than half a century which has now to be considered was one of those short spans of time which encompass the decay of a system of economy which evolved over many centuries. They recur from time to time in history. In this case the 400 years or so from, say, 1450 to 1875, had seen, if not the birth, certainly the childhood, the adolescence and the full manhood of yeoman farming undertaken for the profit of the owner-occupier or the tenant of the acres under cultivation or pasture. The emphasis had moved periodically from corn to stock and back to corn; but all the time the prime motive behind the ploughing and seeding and harvesting, behind the mating, birth and rearing of beast and sheep and pig was the profit to be made in the process. And the incentive of the money-bag, although much despised, is by no means always evil in its results. Allied to an incalculable measure of pride in the achievement of a fine tilthy seed-bed, a yield of grain greater than one's neighbour's, of stock bred to give more milk or meat or wool than ever before, it raised British farming from the depths of medieval mediocrity to the heights of the middle nineteenth century when it was both the envy and the object lesson of the whole world.

In these centuries the profit—and it was usually a comparatively easy profit—was there for the taking, because there was a ready market to hand for all the food that could be grown. As farm production rose, so did the number of mouths to be fed. There was, it is true, always some competition from one's neighbours; but by and large the supply ran so little ahead of the demand that there was rarely a surplus to depress prices excessively. When, in later years, foreign competitors hove in sight and the grain of the Scandinavian and other European countries appeared likely to incommode the British farmer, the landed influence in Parliament was strong enough to secure the erection of a tariff barrier against the wheat from Dantzig or Rouen. And, of course, through all this farming for profit there ran a thin thread of farming for self-subsistence, continued from the days when agriculture was pursued for this one purpose alone. The mid-Victorian yeoman's wife baked her bread from the wheat that her husband grew, brewed beer from his barley, dressed the beef and mutton that had come from his pastures, and cured the bacon that had fattened in his styes. But for most men and women in the British countryside these days were on the way out, or had gone; and the village grocer was fast replacing the village fields as the immediate, perceptible source of the food of the villagers. And the townsman had for centuries been fed from the shop and market stall. But, in general, the farmer grew crops and stock for sale; and the market was, except in years of unusually good harvest, strong enough to give him a profit which varied from adequate to princely according to season and supply. It seemed almost incidental that in farming for a profit each British yeoman was making his own small contribution to the pool of national subsistence. Indeed, only a handful of statesmen and economists were at any one time conscious of this role which the great body of yeomen farmers was playing upon the national stage. Only upon the rare occasions of real or imagined dearth did a conscious conception of the man in the field as the provisioner of the state encroach upon popular thought. Such times were those when the Tudors viewed the growth of sheep and the decay of corn with concern, or when Napoleon brought the country within distant view of starvation. At all other times the British farmer and the part he played in feeding a soaring population were largely taken for granted; but they had not been undervalued in spite of being so much out of mind.

The thought was expressed occasionally by the statesman, but rarely in popular print, except, curiously, in that intended for reading by the rural squire or the husbandman himself. Thus Markham, the mid-seventeenth-century agricultural hack, could write that 'the labours of the Husbandman giveth libertie to all Vocations, Arts, Mysteries and Trades, to follow their several functions with peace and industrie'. The reason that the farmer and his occupation were taken so much for granted was the simple one that agriculture was so much an integral part of the life of the nation that it was unnecessary to express what everyone subconsciously knew. No one hymned the praises of the clothier or the cook; so why should Hodge have his paean? It was only when the land and its life became exotic plants in an urban civilization that they also became the objects of reverence to the mystics among men; and the worship of John Barleycorn revived, a strange resurgence of the most primitive of all cults, because a generation sceptical of the sedatives of conventional religion sees in it a reality to be placed upon the altar in substitution for the wafer and the wine. But this hyperromantic approach to the countryside is regrettable when it conceives of the people as made for the land and not the land for the people.

The immensely healthy system of national subsistence through virtually non-competitive profit farming flourished in greater or less degree from at least the days of the Wars of the Roses to the time when the soldiers of Britain were fighting imperial battles in the snows of the Crimea. It broke down so quickly that for many years even the wisest of men could not see that it had gone for ever; or at least in the form that they and their forefathers had known it. The causes of the collapse of British national-subsistence farming were beyond British control; but the remedy was not. That the remedy was not applied was due in some measure to faults within the body of the rural community.

It is necessary to cast the mind back for a few moments to pick up some scattered threads in time, threads which were

slowly woven into a cloak of antipathy towards the fate
of British agriculture, a cloak which was in turn the dis-
tinctive dress of the townsman of late Victorian days and
of almost every other townsman until very recent years.
First, these same dwellers in the mean streets of Birmingham
and Manchester and all the other stinking urban slums were
the children or the grandchildren of those cottagers and
commoners who were dispossessed by the enclosures of the
late eighteenth and early nineteenth centuries; and the
humiliation and poverty, misery and injustice of those days
were become a folk memory which still rankled; or, themselves forgotten, had bred a hostility to commercial agriculture which was none the less bitter for being without
conscious foundation. Second, the widespread and ingenious
propaganda of the Anti-Corn Law League had implanted
in the artisan and other members of the urban middle and
lower classes a firm belief in the anti-social greed of the
landowner and the farmer. It had been the avowed intention
of the corn laws to maintain grain prices at an artificially
high level; dear wheat meant dear bread; and dear bread was
blamed for the poverty of the urban labourer and his family.
The chain of cause and effect could be disproved with ease,
but the men and women in the towns had more faith in their
intuition than in an economist's arguments, even if they could
understand them. Third, a nation which was becoming
humane in its view of the sufferings of any of its members
looked at the farm labourer and saw in him the third member
of the agricultural partnership, but a partner who was poorly
rewarded for his work, who lived as near the bone as anyone
in the land, but one whose labours brought a very rich
return for the senior partners, the farmer and the landlord.
And, fourth, there was the farmer himself. The vanities of
prosperity have been one of the frequent but intrinsically
harmless vices of the yeomen of England. Cobbett's acid
criticism of the ostentatious wealth of the rustic masters of his

day in comparison with the simple, honest comfort of their somewhat less wealthy fathers will barely stand repetition. It was in some ways unjust, because the early nineteenth-century farmer had enough capital invested in his enterprise to be entitled to expect a dividend upon it that was large in the eyes of those who still thought of him as a rural craftsman in a very modest way. But Cobbett had sufficient foundation for his cynicism to make his views ones which were widely and honestly held.

An age which was reaching out to new efficiencies also looked askance at the bucolic stolidity of the husbandman who was so often out of touch with the times. Mary Russell Mitford's Mrs. Sally descanted upon the merits of the flail wielded by a stout right arm, and attributed the misfortunes of her parish to the invention of the seed drill and the threshing machine. And Hoskyn's man draining on Clay Farm scorned good advice with a surly echo of the conservative rustics of all ages: 'I've been a-draining this forty year, and I ought to know summat about it.' These were attitudes of mind which may have amused but which certainly antagonized those to whom appeals to help the ruined farmer were made. The urban refusal to tolerate a penny on the loaf in order to save British agriculture was understandable, however fundamentally it was in error. Victorian Britain pursued its gods seriously and sincerely, but they were often hard and sometimes strange gods: respectability, bred by evangelism upon the puritan conscience; self-help, sought from within the individual soul and not from the corporate state without; a pathetic belief in progress; and the *idée fixe* that free trade was not a temporary expedient but an ultimate truth upon whose altar even the nation's own land and the welfare of the men who farmed it must be sacrificed if necessary. And each of these gods caused its worshippers to look critically at the agricultural community. Respectability, because so often the poor, wretched labourer was human enough to drown his sorrows in the pot: 'I knows I drinks beer, and so would anybody else in my place; it makes me kinder stupid, as I don't feel nothing then', as Richard Jefferies recorded the speech of a labourer in the dock for beating his wife while in drink. Self-help, because the farmer was a notorious supplicant for aid in adversity. Progress, for it was easy to demonstrate the backwardness of much agriculture. And the King Charles's head of free trade, for what was farming but yet another business which must take its chance in the world.

Let us now turn to the great collapse of British arable farming, set as it was against the mental background sketched above. A combination of circumstances had worked to keep home-grown grain a profitable commodity even after the repeal of the corn laws, chief among them being the Crimean and Franco-German wars, which had reduced continental surpluses and maintained home prices. A combination of circumstances also temporarily concealed the direction from which the blow came in the middle 1870's. Stock disease, disastrous harvests, and the depth of a world-wide cycle of agricultural depression came at exactly the same time as the American prairies were preparing to pour out their first great harvests of wheat. The pioneers of the Mid-western plains moved steadily westward and cropped the virgin land exactly as prehistoric man had cleared and sown the reclaimed land of Europe, by burning the forest overgrowth and harrowing the seed into the topsoil of leaf-mould and wood ash. The development of machinery solved the prairie grower's greatest problem, that of labour for sowing and harvesting. And the new American railway lines, which extended their mileage from 30,800 in 1860 to 94,200 in 1880, transported the grain at less than the actual cost of freightage in order to stimulate settlement in the areas alongside the tracks. And at the ports of the eastern seaboard of the United

States grain was shipped to Liverpool at rates which were cut by nearly two-thirds in the twelve years from 1873 to 1884. The result was that wheat from America could be moved to Britain at little more than 7s. or 8s. a quarter. British wheat in the first five years of the 1870's averaged 55s. a quarter. American wheat could be grown on grossly exploited virgin prairie soils for at least half this price and still show a profit to the grower; so that even with the addition of the transatlantic freight charges the New World could still knock the bottom out of the markets of the Old World. And when disease and bad harvests ended the bottom was seen to have fallen out of the British cereal market.

There was only one certain answer to the flood of American grain, and it was one which almost no one conceded to be a possible one—tariff protection. Britain conceived herself to be in a very different position from her European neighbours; as indeed she was, fortunately in some respects, unfortunately in others. France had, by revolution, turned herself into a community of free peasants; Denmark had achieved the same result by the action of a benevolent monarchy, and so had other European states. In all of them the balance between the land and the factory was still heavily weighed down on the side of the land; and it was kept that way because the state frontiers, with few natural defences, demanded the maintenance of a hardy country stock which could quickly be put under arms. The response of Continental governments to the American threat was immediate: an adequate measure of protection. The European peasantry, as a result, remained as prosperous as they had been before the American Middle West was opened up to the corn drill and the reaper, and before the new railroads into Chicago were jammed with the harvested grain. That prosperity never approached that of the English yeoman at the height of his Victorian affluence, but it somewhat exceeded that of the British farm labourer of the time. Britain, indeed, was soon to learn the truth of Fuller's imagery in that the Continental governments, in nourishing their peasants, sowed hydra's teeth wherefrom would rise up armed men for the service of their kingdoms.

Cheap imported meat followed cheap imported grain into Britain in a few years' time. The British stock-farmer had long been falling behind in the task of keeping the nation fed with all the meat it ate, and from the middle of the nineteenth century imports of live cattle from Denmark, Holland, and even—with incredible suffering to the beasts —from America had been rising steadily. The British pedigree stock-breeder had been supplying the new lands with foundation animals from his own incomparable herds and flocks until the plains of North and South America were teeming with white-faced Herefords and rich red Short-horns, and the sweet grasses of New Zealand were feeding Southdown and Kent sheep by the hundred thousand. By the middle 1880's beef beast and sheep could be slaughtered where they had been reared and fattened and loaded to Britain in the newly invented refrigerator ships, which kept the carcases frozen or chilled. Another of the natural barriers of distance which had kept the home market as the preserve of the home grower of grain and meat was down; the world was become Britain's larder; and the labour of old Markham's husbandman 'who giveth libertie to all Voca-tions, Arts, Mysteries and Trades, to follow their several functions with peace and industrie' was become the labour of the Yankee rancher, of the New Zealand flockmaster, and in due course that of the gauchos of the Argentine and of the coolies of the Punjab.

A protective tariff would have kept the flood of foreign grain and meat out of Britain, except that which was needed to supplement home-grown produce; and it would have kept the British farmer on his old cereal legs and his land in full cultivation. But, as has been noted, protection of farm produce appeared to be a quite impossible step to take. Opinion was almost unanimous in rejecting the agricultural demand for a tariff on cereals in particular. The reason was a threefold one.

The urban hostility to farming, arising from the causes noted above, drew from a leader-writer in *Farmer and Stock-Breeder* in 1882 the remark that 'the task of converting the predominant urban population of Great Britain to a belief in the essentiality of agricultural prosperity must needs be a difficult one seeing how strong are the prejudices separating town and country'. In the month in which he wrote, January, the average price of English wheat was 29s. 6d. a quarter, less than half the annual average of twenty years before and less than a quarter of the price which had been made three years before the Battle of Waterloo. Second, the doctrine of *laissez-faire* was a sacrosanct one; certainly not one to be set aside at the behest of so unimportant a body of men as the farmers of Britain. And, third, foreign grain and meat had to be taken in payment for British exports; and to reduce the amount of wheat and beef and mutton which came into the ports would strangle a considerable section of industry, not to mention the raising of its wages bill which would follow the necessity for the urban worker to pay more for home-grown food than he was spending on imported food. And as, by 1891, agriculture accounted for only 10 per cent. of the employed men and women of Britain, a depression in farm-ing could affect only a small proportion of the people of the United Kingdom. The farmer must look after himself, as the ironmaster and the cotton-spinner had to. What was all this fuss about? Rider Haggard, than whom there was no more staunch champion of the farmer and the land, admitted in 1902 that 'protection in Britain, as Britain is now, is an impossibility'; and he thought that free trade had become so integral a part of the nation's life that to abandon it 'would result in something very like a civil war'. Eleven years later the chairman of the Liberal-inspired Land Enquiry Committee, Dyke Acland, wrote: 'There is no evidence that the [agricultural] classes were benefited by the corn laws, or could be helped by their revival. The imposition of food taxes at the cost of the industrial population is by the admission of all parties outside practical politics.'

As it was, the British farmer was left to struggle as best he could against overwhelming odds, or, as Haggard put it, to fight against the mills of God. He was forced to abandon his old adherence to grain-growing because the market had gone out of his control. From the very beginnings of agriculture more than 4,000 years before, the demand for bread grains, ale grains, and cereals for stock had been met by a home supply which was usually adequate, but rarely more than that. In later days the corn-merchant had exercised some influence upon the trend of prices; but in the main the proceeds from the harvest were steady, with high prices for small yields and low prices for plentiful crops. The market was in the collective control of the body of the nation's farmers because the quantity of grain which the agricultural community placed upon it determined the price at which the grain was sold. Now that was all changed. Imported grain fixed the prices at which the British arable farmer could sell his produce; wheat had become an international commodity; and because the bulk of it was grown cheaply by the extensive exploitation of virgin soils in the New World, the agricultural economy of those nations in the Old World which did not protect their farmers by artificial means was completely undermined. This new order of things which brought chaos to British farming can now be seen to be only a passing phase in world economy, a short chapter in international history. But to two generations of British farmers who took their wheat to market to receive for it very often less than it had cost to grow, it seemed as if the ground had been swept away from beneath their feet for ever, and that they and their kind would never again be important—essential—members of the society which they had led for so many centuries.

It would be tedious, and indeed unnecessary to the theme to describe in detail the course of prices and the depths to which agriculture and the condition of the land sank during the decades between the 1870's and the First World War. They are fully set out in a score of books; and they are still within the memory of many. Wheat prices tumbled steadily to a minimum of 22*s*. 10*d*. a quarter in 1894; and meat prices declined, but not so violently as those of grain. The result was a tremendous fall in the intensity of farming. Arable land everywhere went out of cultivation, and nowhere more so than on the heavier clays, where, although yields were high, much labour had to be spent upon the cereal crop. The plough was completely forsaken in the western counties; which was by no means a regrettable result of depression, for Nature never intended the pastoral counties to grow corn. Where arable land tumbled down, poor natural grasses grew up to provide grazing of a sort; buildings decayed, fences were broken down and remained unmended; hedges grew out of hand; ditches and drains silted up and were not cleared; rushes and scrub sprang up where none had been seen for centuries; and improvement came to a standstill. The land of Britain became a vast rural slum. Landlords drew what rents they could. Tenants snatched a profit where it could be found and ceased to farm in so far as that verb connotes a systematic, planned, and intensive use of the soil. The labourer, perhaps, suffered least of all, for he could always hive off into a town to work, and the national policy of cheap food suited his pocket.

The effect upon the three sections of the agricultural community may be examined in a little more detail. The landlord, if he was to keep his land in any sort of use, was forced to concede rebates in rent with every drop in tenants' returns. The pendulum, indeed, swung violently from the one side where it had been for two centuries—that in which the owner of a landed estate was a rural despot, in a position to dictate terms of tenancy and levels of rent to his tenantry —to the opposite extreme, in which landlordism became, except for the social dignities and amenities it conferred, an asset of no value; indeed, very much of a liability. On the eve of the great depression, in 1874-5, a few more than 2,000 persons owned half the agricultural land of England and Wales as a result of 200 years of steady accretion pursued in times when agricultural prosperity was high, rents remunerative, and estate farming itself a profitable occupation. Now that was all ended. If rent rebates were not granted, tenants deserted their farms; and the profit had gone out of farming one's land on one's own account. The landlords thereupon began to divest themselves of their liabilities at an increasing rate. By 1912, even though some measure of prosperity was then returning, nearly 200,000 acres of land were being sold every year. And the area of England and Wales farmed by the owners of the land fell from 15 per cent. in 1887 to 10 per cent. in 1912. That the landlord did not unburden himself of his property even more rapidly was due to two causes: the tradition of squirearchy was too old to be broken easily; and the non-economic advantages of land ownership were still present. The tenant farmer had often been able to rent land at a lower cost than that at which he could buy it and pay the interest on his mortgage because the landlord voluntarily sacrificed part of the return on his capital in payment for his rural sports and his rural dignity.

The landlords' capital was also shrinking, both as the intrinsic value of land fell and also as maintenance lagged behind and the fixed equipment of the estate decayed. The landlord had often enough in the piping days neglected his duty towards the irreplaceable national asset which he held in trust; now he was often becoming financially incapable of doing that duty. And, ironically, the society which had criticized but tolerated him, his unique position, and his regard or lack of it for his obligations to the land in the past, this same society which through its own neglect had placed him in no condition to fulfil those obligations under the new dispensation whispered the words 'land nationalization' more and more frequently. Nationalization of the ownership of land remains a topic of controversy into our own day, and many words in print and speech have been spilled over it. Too many, perhaps, for what matters is how the land is used and not who owns it—private landlord, college, Church, or state. Whoever of these permits and encourages the farmer to pursue his calling in peace, in reasonable prosperity, and with high efficiency and takes no more than his fair return upon the money he has invested, then he or it is a good landlord and deserves well of the community. If he wilfully fails in these things, he is an enemy to society and should be divested of his acres.

Not all the landlords suffered as acutely as the owners of the smaller estates on the East Anglian clays, which were hardest hit of all. Rents in the pastoral counties were fairly well maintained because the tenants here were livestock men who, while they lost a little income from the abandonment of their cereal crops, still had the foundations of their herds and flocks to support them; and costs of production played a far less important part in their economy. They had lived in modest comfort for many generations. Indeed, their condition had improved steadily since the urban demand for meat grew large and the stock-improvers had placed in their hands better raw materials with which to meet the need. The price of meat fell somewhat with the advent of refrigerated mutton from New Zealand and chilled beef from the Argentine; but the fall in price was counteracted by the cheaper feeding-stuffs which the stock-feeders were able to buy as a result of the collapse of the cereal market.

These stock-men were exceptions, and by no means in-considerable exceptions, to the general depression of British agriculture. Their difficulties were real, but not disastrous, as were those of their cereal brethren. The problems of survival which faced the men who had won their livings from the plough appeared to be insoluble, as indeed they sometimes were. There were, however, two ways out of the impasse for many of them. One was an intensification of cereal production. The other was a change to a form of agricultural production which stood in no jeopardy from foreign competition. Neither was an easy way to take. In-tensification meant in effect the growing of more grain at lower cost than before, so that the wheat or barley could be produced for sale at a small margin of profit even at the new low prices. It called for a profound change in farming methods. The old lavish use of labour, the perfect cultivations by which no weed was left, the use of expensively made farmyard manure all had to go. In their place there had to come the new machinery of steam ploughing in fields enlarged to take full advantage of the mechanical power, which was something which more nearly approached the scratch farming of the American plains than the high agriculture of the Victorian heyday; and a generous use of the new 'artificial fertilizers' which were now freely available. By these means grain could be grown more cheaply and in greater quantities. It was given to few men to have the courage to throw aside the comfortable and satisfying old ways of arable agriculture; the foresight to realize that the piping days had gone for ever—or at least for a generation or more—and that the sooner the ancient garments of farm-ing method were doffed and the new ones donned the better; or the knowledge to put the new methods into force.

The old ways were dead; but they continued to move convulsively for many years in their rustic coffins. The careful ploughing by well-matched teams of Shires and

Suffolks with their polished brasses and gleaming traces; the neat hedges of quick and holly, blackthorn and hornbeam that had grown and thickened and been laid times without number; the army of reapers working in the field and drinking at the harvest home; the yards of bullocks fed with linseed cake from strange lands so that they could trample down the straw beneath their hooves into muck for the enrichment of an English field—all these things were finished. And the ironic part of it was that the nation that killed them later turned upon the farmer and laid at his door the blame for the abandonment of the 'natural' order of husbandry and the decay of the rural community which was conceived to have flourished under that order. Much that was good and fine and irreplaceable was killed, but the farmer was not the self-appointed executioner, but the involuntary and unwilling instrument of the national interest, or lack of it.

The conquest of distance which had brought the American larder to the British kitchen had not, however, gone far enough to destroy the home monopoly in perishable foods; but it had proceeded sufficiently to bring the dairy farmers and vegetable-growers of distant counties within reach of the great urban markets. Here, in fact, lay the second solution to the problem of agricultural depression. The great dairying districts of the island had already a very great history behind them. The Vale of the White Horse was the home of its great cheeses even when it emerged into recorded history; and the Cheddar dairy industry was almost as old. These and the other pastoral areas had hitherto, however, lain beyond the reach of a sufficient liquid milk market, and had had to concentrate upon the export of milk in its processed and less profitable forms, as butter and cheese. The railways swept down these old barriers of distance, and from the middle of the nineteenth century the country dairy farm came to be in a position to compete with and eventually to supplant the filthy town dairies which flourished in London and the dairywomen who sat in the metropolitan parks and milked their cows for the refreshment of the passers-by. The immensity of the opportunity which the railways gave was not immediately realized, nor was the fact that here was a market for country produce which was beyond the reach of the Americas or the Antipodes. It needed the combination of acute cereal depression and the vivid example of the success of the army of Scotsmen who came south to find a comparative prosperity producing milk from the tumbled-down grass of the old arable farms on the Essex and Hertfordshire clays, to break down the prejudice of the bullock-and-wheat men against the despised cow-keeper. In time this liquid milk industry—and even its most successful practitioner would not for years agree that it was more than a rural industry—was to become the major constituent in the compendium of pursuits which make up British agriculture.

It must be admitted that in one way at least depression served the ultimate cause of good, natural farming well enough. In spite of the high yields of cereal crops which British fields give as a result of careful cultivation, adequate manuring, and a high natural fertility, many of these fields are not natural cereal lands except in the drier eastern counties. They are pre-eminently fitted to growing good grass. It needed the collapse of the wheat and feeding barley market in the 1870's to banish the plough from its annual progression over fields in which it should be only an occasional visitor, and to substitute for it good grass to make the magnificent beef and mutton that Britain can grow better than anyone else, and the milk which was to play so large and beneficial a part in the dietary of later generations. Good grass which feeds the cheapest meat and produces the cheapest milk was, of course, not immediately grown, and it is still far from being universal. Nature needed more than a little help here, as in many other directions. But pioneers

were already at work evolving the seeds mixtures and the
new strains which make one leaf of grass now more nutritious
than two were before.

An intermediate stage, based on principles established in
the high Victorian days, had to work out its course before
British agriculture was able to resume the path of self-sufficient independence which it abandoned when the first foreign
feeding-stuffs came in, beginning with the linseed cake of
the late eighteenth century. The mid-Victorian farmer had
won a new fertility for his land not only from the new imported artificial fertilizers, but also from passing foreign
protein-rich feeds through his stock to make manure. In
time the decline of the cereal market placed other feeding-
stuffs at the disposal of the grazier and the milk man; and
both the cheap imported wheat offals and barleys and the
ruinously cheap home-grown cereals enabled him to grow
his meat and produce his milk from bread and ale grains
brought in from outside, and to use his land as no more than
the exercising grounds of his stock, their summer bedrooms
and the dining-rooms where they ate of alien but highly
nutritious foods. When this period has receded far enough
back in time to enable it to be viewed in proper perspective,
it may be seen to be one of the more regrettable, but perhaps
necessary, phases of British agriculture. Necessary because
it was the only way in which many farmers managed to
scrape a living at all; regrettable because it broke the natural
circle of husbandry and bred and sustained a sense of
essential dependence on foreign feeding-stuffs which the
sharp lessons of two wars have not yet finally dispelled.

There, then, are the tenant farmers, broken ships drifting
with the curse of Cobden upon them in the unkind free
trade winds, grateful for the havens of the milk trade, of
turning cheap oil cakes into meat, of the brussels sprout and
potato market: very different men indeed from the independent, parlour-furnishing, proud yeomen of the piping

years between the winter days when Florence Nightingale was bringing comfort to the men in the hospitals of the Crimea and the time when the Prussian armies were at the gates of Paris. Behind the broken yeomanry are the landlords, once princes of English acres, to be curtsied to as they moved up the church path and to be feared for their power to turn out a tenant through spite for an independently-cast vote or an imagined slight; a class now moving into the Edwardian twilight of the great country houses, coming to be bereft of their political power, but still a stabilizing force, the inheritors of a long tradition of straight dealing in a world given over to new commercial, opportunist gods. There remains the labourer in the fields, once inarticulate, but now fast finding a collective voice, some measure of domestic comfort, but none of his old independence.

The most remarkable thing about the farm labourers was that large numbers of them were ceasing to be farm labourers. The exodus of the worker from the land, which had been in progress for centuries, was accentuated by the agricultural slump and the inevitable decline of the amount of work to be done on the land. Dog-and-stick farming, or even seven days a week of penal servitude in the cowshed, needed fewer hands than the laborious work on the arable farm; but they relieved the lot of the labourer to the extent that his employment became more regular and less seasonal. The net result of the reduction of the labour force on the farm was that in the last twenty years of the nineteenth century the number of agricultural labourers in England and Wales fell by a little more than one quarter, from 830,452 in 1881 to 609,105 in 1901. Contemporaries with a feeling for the land and a nostalgia for the vanished luxuriance of British farming saw in this a catastrophe. It was asserted that the pick of the men were leaving the countryside for the towns, and that agriculture was faced with a shortage of manpower. If it was, it was for the first time in 500 years.

'Only the dullards, the vicious, or the wastrels stay upon the land, because they are unfitted for any other life', Rider Haggard wrote; and he said that the result could only be a progressive deterioration of the race. Time may prove him to be a false prophet in this last matter. But it would seem that the fundamental cause of the depopulation of the countryside was that for the labourer of all men it was a place without hope; and his children might well imagine to be painted on the farm gate the words—if they had known them—that crown the portals of hell. He could exchange his damp and squalid cottage for a home that was little worse, and often better, in town; and although grime and soot replaced the blue sky there was always the music-hall and a bottle of gin for the man with no further ambition, and for the labourer with a purpose a foreman's job and all the domestic amenities that followed, or even a small shop or little business of his own. In the country he could work his back bent and his wife prematurely aged with want and care, and still have nothing to show for it at the end.

This is what the old enclosures had done for the new generation: they had taken the hope and the independence out of life. Once, as George Sturt said, a careful man and wife needed not to despair of becoming rich in the possession of a cow and a pig or two, and of good clothes and household utensils; and they might well expect to see their children grow up strong and prosperous in the peasant way. Where the losses had been barely recognized before, they were now becoming consciously known and increasingly emphasized by universal education and the growth of trade unionism on the farm. Schooling was making the labourer discontented with his lot, not only because it crystallized his thoughts about his condition and made them coherent, and informed him of the happier states of other men, but also because it trained him to be clerkly minded, to despise the plough and corduroys, and to reverence the pen and the white collar. If it had taught

him more of the art of drawing a good furrow and less of the
mechanics of striking an account-book balance, his school
could have kept alive in his heart the spark of craftsmanly
pride of his forefathers and not sent him a-whoring after
strange jobs. But it did not; and here was another reason why
the last place he wanted to see his son was at the plough-
handle.

Much of this was realized by the social reformers; and
remedies were sought. The obvious first cure was still to give
the labourer a proprietary interest in his work. He had been
deprived of his land and he had no longer any right of ownership in the goods he produced. Then let him be given a smallholding. It was not often seriously argued that this would
increase the national production of food. That was hardly
necessary, for the whole world was now Britain's larder. The
smallholding movement was one in a socially desirable
direction, it was said; but there were many sound doubts of
its effectiveness. Civilization had, for better or for worse,
taken the bulk of the rural population beyond the stage at
which they could subsist upon what they produced for themselves; and when a man with 300 good acres could barely
make a living it was certain that a smallholder with 30 acres
of the indifferent land which he was likely to get would be
unable to survive. The protagonists forgot the old argument
which was essential to the case: mixed farming in miniature
gives a mixed farm income in miniature, and only specialist
market gardening upon the soils for which there was already
keen competition could hope to yield a living wage. This, it
may be noted, is not true today, when the profit from dairy
farming, for example, is such as to ensure an adequate
reward to an enterprising, intelligent, and hard-working
man on a few acres. I have one such man in mind who,
beginning life as a farm labourer and saving hard, hired
25 acres of a derelict Welsh valley and with immense labour
and skilful husbandry is now well on the way to farming 250

acres. And there are scores like him. But the turn of the nineteenth and twentieth centuries was not a time to turn a man
loose upon a smallholding; and even if a few might succeed,
it was no general panacea for a universal evil. Successive
Acts were passed to enable local authorities to acquire land
for small farms; but the power on the county councils was too
often in the hands of the members of the upper and middle
rural classes, with vested interests in a wholly dependent
labour force, to make much progress. Feudalism was by
no means dead, and a country parson told the Land
Enquiry Committee in 1913 that the smallholdings Acts
were dead letters in his district, 'being completely vetoed
by the power of the estate. Labourers in these feudal
villages are not regarded as people who should want to
rise.'

Many other solutions to the problem of improving the
conditions of the labourer and attracting good men back to
the land were put forward. A minimum wage was canvassed,
but opposed because farm work was said to be too varied for
a common scale to be laid down, because it would result
in the dismissal of the aged and infirm, because it would
mean the employment of more casual labour, and because
it would force farmers to turn even more to grass and so
employ fewer men. The degree of validity of the several
excuses is self-apparent.

In point of fact, the farm labourer, whatever his lack of
ultimate opportunity, was coming to be materially better
off than he had been for a couple of centuries. His principal
need, food, was cheap; and it was no longer subject to the
vagaries of seasonal fluctuation. The price of the loaf moved
within a range of only 1½d. over many years before the First
World War. Lack of any guarantee of regular employment
was the nightmare that haunted the country cottage; but a
man in permanent work could hope to keep his family fed
in a way which might have seemed poor enough in the eyes

of contemporary investigators used to the plenty of the Edwardian middle-class table, but which today seems good by comparison. In 1907 the wage of the bulk of the farm labourers was between 16*s.* and 29*s.* a week; and although the motto of the villager was said to be 'We don't live; we linger', Mr. Seebohm Rowntree published a large number of specimen budgets from life which give it the present, although perhaps not the contemporary, lie. Here is one taken at random: A Leicestershire man and his wife, with a family of two young boys, had in a typical week 6 lb. of sugar, ½ lb. butter, 6 oz. tea, a pint of new milk a day, 5½ lb. meat, 20 lb. bread, 5½ lb. flour, with many smaller items and much garden produce. Well below the level of plenty, perhaps, but by no means a starvation diet. The labourer was, however, entirely dependent upon his earnings in cash, which were barely or only just adequate for his current needs; and could rarely save up against ill health or old age. Nearly everything he needed had to be bought from a shop, and if he failed to earn he could not buy. This was the difference between him and his forefathers, who grew their own food and clothing and cut their home and their fuel out of the woods, and could be independent of money if they must. This was the true poverty of the farm labourer of the early twentieth century.

The perilous state of agriculture in all its aspects was manifest: in the loss of the ability of the landlord to keep his estate in good condition; in the bankruptcy of the farmer; in the discontent which led to the departure of the labourer for the town; and, as a result of all three, in the ruin of the good land of Britain that had been won from the forest by the sweat of countless generations of pioneers and which, through enforced neglect, was reverting to swamp and scrub, rank grass, and weed-infested ploughland. Even when, in the few years before 1914, some degree of prosperity had returned to agriculture, there was still some well-informed and severe criticism of the standard of farming, for there was too much leeway to make up for it to be done quickly. Amos told the Farmers' Club in 1910 that 'there is no end of land farmed shockingly badly'; and two years later Sir Daniel Hall wrote that 'bad business habits and slipshod management are far too common'. Hall's stricture was a foretaste of much that was to be said about farming in years to come, because agriculture had now become without qualification an industry, and there was no room in it for those who still regarded it as a way of life which gave a profit almost incidentally to its pursuit.

The politicians and the political economists had nearly put British farming out of business: the latter by their active encouragement of a policy of free trade; the former by the fear that too strong an opposition to free trade would lose them the urban vote. *The Times* had declared in 1826 that 'bread must be had cheap', and emphasized it in italics. In 1906 it was still saying it. But it was evident to both economist and the statesman that something must appear to be done to help this dying calling which had once been the very life blood of the nation. Positive assistance was impossible. A tariff wall against cheap foreign food on the French and German lines would never be sanctioned by the townsman. The only possible alternatives were to inculcate some degree of self-help into agriculture; to give what overt financial aid was practicable; and to disguise the paucity of the imagination and courage among statesmen in this matter by as large a shoal of red herrings as could be drawn over the trail—and there were always plenty of simple, earnest folk there to draw them. The formula was to declare 'there is no royal road back to agricultural prosperity; variety is the essence of the matter'. The red herrings then followed: greater security of tenure for the tenant, tithe reform, partial derating, small holdings, agricultural education. All were very helpful and very necessary, but none came within a mile of the heart of the problem—the losing battle against foreign grain and meat grown cheaply and sold at prices with which home produce could never compete. The beginnings of a nation-wide chain of agricultural education were made. The new Board of Agriculture, which had evolved in a typically English way out of a department of the Home Office founded in 1865 to deal with the cattle plague of that year, timidly ventured into the revolutionary field of indirect state help for agriculture, under the scathing tongues of Rider Haggard and others. When this Norfolk squire with an intense passion for the welfare of the land turned his pen from chronicling the exploits of the white queens of mysterious Africa to considering the remedies for the depression in farming, he suggested that 'the President of the Board of Agriculture might be something more than a compiler of labour statistics, an officer for the enforcement of regulations as to diseased cattle, a disseminator of useful information about beetles, and a peripatetic utterer of speeches at agricultural shows'. The Board, by initiating steps for the prevention of disease, by technical instruction, by shouldering the growing burden of research which had been carried so manfully in the past by a handful of workers, by all these things they helped the farmer to grow more; but they could not help him to produce at a sufficient profit in a market which was so strongly against him.

A string of statutes aimed at giving the tenant a secure tenure of his land and freedom to crop it as he liked. In fact, all that was given was compensation for the improvements the tenant had made and for unreasonable disturbance unless for good and sufficient reasons of estate management. But the landlord's consent had to be obtained before improvements were made; and notice to quit upon the sale of land so that vacant possession could be offered to the purchaser was held to come within the definition of good estate management. The Liberals, those ancient enemies of the rural landlord, demanded complete security for tenants by state-aided purchase, by nationalization of the land and the granting of tenancies under the state, or by fixity of tenure subject only to interference by an impartial, independent land court. The third solution was, in the course of years, to be adopted; but only after two world wars. Time has played into the hands of the tenant farmer, who emphatically did not desire the first solution of state-aided purchase, or, rather less strongly perhaps, that of state landlordship. The lot of the owner-occupier has its advantages and its disadvantages. Capital is rarely plentiful in a farming enterprise, and it is foolish to tie it up in land purchase when land can be rented and the capital left free for day-to-day farming; but a man is readier to improve his own buildings than those of another. In good times the security of occupation which ownership alone could give was sometimes desirable; but in days of uncertainty or adversity it was an asset to be able to cut one's losses and clear out, for which reason even long leases were not always sought. And also in favour of tenancy against ownership there were the facts that rents were often not the full economic return on the landlord's investment because he sacrificed something to gain the sporting rights and social dignity of land ownership; and that a landlord could be asked for a rent rebate when produce prices fell but the owner-occupier had to bear all his burdens himself.

In point of fact, some little measure of agricultural prosperity returned as the first decade of the twentieth century proceeded. The credit for it must go first to a general rise in world prices, including those for food; and, second, to the working out of the process of readjustment of British farming from the Victorian emphasis on wheat to the Edwardian dependence on an opportunist cropping and the production of meat and milk from cheap cereals and imported feeds. Sir Daniel Hall, an agricultural contributor to *The Times*

in the great lineage of Caird, Fream, and Charles Mac-
donald, went through Britain in 1912 as Caird had done
sixty years before and Haggard at the beginning of the
century, and he summed up his impressions of the financial
condition of farming thus: 'To a man who takes the trouble
to learn and attend to his business, farming now offers every
prospect of a good return upon his capital.'

Whatever the financial return the farmer got for his crops,
his output was surprisingly large considering under what dis-
couragements he had been working, the decline of careful
and full land use, and the fact that farming had ceased to be
of any real consequence in the life of the nation. In 1851 the
20 million people of England, Wales, and Scotland had been
as completely fed from the island's soil as made no matter.
In 1911 the population had risen to almost exactly double
that of 1851, a little over 40 million. The British farmer was
now feeding the British people with 58 per cent. of their
barley, 79 per cent. of their oats, 61 per cent. of their beef,
54 per cent. of their mutton and lamb, 95 per cent. of their
milk, nearly all their potatoes, but only 21 per cent. of their
wheat and flour. With the exception of bread corn, the
British farmer was really not doing too badly; and the
decline in wheat production was offset by the greatly increased output of milk and potatoes to meet a soaring
demand for these commodities. The change from production
upon medieval, bread-conscious lines to the production of a
varied modern dietary was well on the way to completion,
with inestimable benefit to the pocket of farming and the
health of the nation. A comparison on a starch equivalent
basis would probably show the farmer to be feeding at least
as many people before the First World War as he had done
during the Crimean War. Till the middle of the nineteenth
century he had kept his production in step with the growth in
population, and he improved and extended his farming so
that each new mouth could be fed from British soil. It was

one of the great tragedies of the era that he was not permitted to continue to keep level in the race between his production and the population.

How immense a catastrophe might have been the involuntary dereliction of the British farmer no one realized until 1917. The nation went into the First World War with the comfortable thought that whatever might be the unhappy fate of the temporary heroes in the trenches, at least those at home would have their bellies filled as usual by the wheat of America and India, the meat of Argentine, and the butter and cheese of New Zealand. The success of the German submarines in interrupting the flow of this foreign food to Britain shook the complacency of those who had paid no more than lip-service to the cause of efficient agricultural production. As the war progressed *laissez-faire* farming, under the stimulus of scarcity prices, raised its output of food very greatly indeed; but it was obvious that even more must be done if Britain was not to lose the war at the dinner table at home. By a lucky chance, two men of imagination and courage were at the Board of Agriculture at the time: Lord Ernle, the great agricultural historian, and Daniel Hall, than whom no one knew better what the land of Britain was capable of growing if it was given the opportunity. A food production department, backed by the legislative authority of the Corn Production Act, became in effect the national director of British agriculture, with county committees as the local directors and the farmers themselves little more than the day-to-day managers of their land. The department stabilized rents; it provided—perhaps prematurely—tractors to hasten work on the land and additional hands to supplement the farm labour force, which was inadequate for the new intensive farming and which was further depleted by the call of high wages on other work; it controlled the nature of the crops grown by compulsory orders; it guaranteed both markets and prices for all that the farmer could grow; and, not least of all, it founded an agricultural wages board to fix a minimum wage for the farm labourer.

Some of these innovations were obviously expedients of wartime, to be thrown aside when peace returned. But others were no less obviously essential elements in the foundation of a bright new age for agriculture in the post-war world. It seemed as though the nation had learnt its lesson; and that the ghost of hunger which stalked through the land had led to no less a renunciation of the sins of commission and omission of the past and as great an embracement of a new resolve to father the land against a greedy world than the ghost of Jacob Marley had awakened in the heart of Dickens's miser. The townsman had had a bad fright; but events were very soon to show that fear, whatever it may achieve in fiction, does not lead to repentance and a change of heart in men of flesh and blood. In the event, the years from 1916 to 1919 were only an interlude in a sordid, discreditable story, albeit a prophetic interlude; the brief surge of virility in a chronically sick industry to which a stimulant was administered, but which when the stimulant had worn off, was in a state as bad as before. And the folly of it was that the sick man was the great, ultimate, and only breadwinner of the past; and he very might well become so again in the future.

CHAPTER EIGHT

Blueprints for a
New Agriculture

THE TWENTY-ONE years between the end of the First
World War and the beginning of the second were the
period of a paradox. British farming, emerging
triumphant and confident from its testing time from 1917
onwards, was abandoned almost overnight; and continued
in a dark wilderness. And yet at no time in recent history had
the people taken so keen an interest in the land and in the
most ancient of all industries which was pursued upon it.
Agriculture languished neglected—or was at best kept from
complete decay by random and opportunist palliatives—
and yet the townsman was absorbing a new farming literature
and calling for more. The note of rural authenticity had
rarely been struck in the past. Men had been either too close to
or too far from the soil to relish reading of its hardships and joys.

186

Only occasionally had a Sturt or a Jefferies or a Hardy emerged to write of things as they were; and they had often dealt with the people rather than their pursuits. Now, however, the pellucid prose of Adrian Bell; the vigorous expression of personal experience of A. G. Street; the accurate and sensitive chronicles of incursions into rurality of Crichton Porteous and Thomas Firbank; and the white-hot fervour of H. J. Massingham, sometimes misguided but never insincere; these, a few equal, a host of inferior pens and minds brought the men and women of urban and suburban Britain into a new vicarious relationship with the land and the farmer.

Side by side with the imaginative literary approach ran a steady stream of practical plans for the land, of grim prophets of impending doom, of *laudatores temporis acti*, of sternly realistic economists with blueprints for a new structure of rural society, of back-to-the-landers and down-with-the-landlorders, of simple-lifers and composters who saw the mark of Cain on every bag of fertilizer, of anthologists of poets in prose and verse with birds in their binoculars or bees in their bonnets. It went on and on, in books, in the newspapers, on the radio. Many of the pens and voices were negligible. Some did much harm to the cause they sought to help because when John Smith of Peckham took his family to the country they found that they could not lean on a farm gateway and chew straw because the gateway was ankle deep in mud and the straw did not bring the visions it should. A few were highly important contributions to rural salvation: Astor and Rowntree with their reasoned analysis of the situation in the 'thirties; the land nationalization campaigns of Orwin and Daniel Hall; the little-heeded but occasionally prophetic voice of the Rural Reconstruction Association; and the quiet encouragement of Scott Watson. Could British agriculture have been saved in prose it would have entered into an immediate millennium.

The period began with a new and apparently hopeful situation. By the end of the First World War nearly 3 million acres of grassland had been ploughed up. There was an inevitable decline in production of meat and milk; but in the bread grains British self-sufficiency had been raised from eleven weeks in the year in 1916-17 to eighteen weeks in 1918-19. The combination of state direction and help, of the attraction of profitable prices and the patriotism of the man on the land had brought about a remarkable revival in agriculture. It was a revival of which the outward signs were hundreds of thousands more acres of brown arable, yellow grain, and green potato haulm than had been seen in the countryside for sixty years, and the patent—and sometimes blatant—prosperity of the farmer. Could it last? To the agricultural eye it seemed that it must, for world prices for grain were even higher than those paid to the British farmer in wartime; and the guarantees of a frightened and hunger-threatened nation were now succeeded by an Agriculture Act in 1920 which protected the cereal-grower against loss. Must not the gratitude of 40 million people saved from starvation be a sure shield against neglect in the future? It seemed that the answer to the question must be 'Yes'. In the event it was 'No'. Distant countries outside the war zone began to inundate the open British market again with grain, and prices fell to a level at which the honouring of the guarantees of the Agriculture Act would have cost the nation £20 million in the first year. Public opinion jettisoned what shreds of thankful goodwill it may have retained for a rural section of society which was not alone in throwing money to the four winds, and forced the Government to abandon the Act even before it came into effective operation. With the price guarantees to the farmer went also the minimum wage rate guarantees to the farm labourer. Farming was back where it had been in 1914. It was a betrayal of faith which was to have a profound effect on the subconscious agricultural mind for a generation to come; and greying heads that remembered 1920 were full of scepticism at the fair words which were spoken again in 1947.

In retrospect, the optimism of 1920 is seen to be obviously ill founded. The war had ended with four men out of every five living in the towns, and with only one man in fifteen working on a farm. The aura of romanticism engendered by a generation of printed sentiment and sentimentality did not yet surround the man on the land or the land itself. World economics were not yet throwing Britain back upon her own resources. And another war seemed remote, if not impossible. Almost any premium at all upon an insurance policy of self-sufficiency that was no longer necessary must obviously seem excessive. The factory won yet another victory over the field, for what Sir George Stapledon has called the co-efficient of ruralicity was far too near zero for it to be otherwise.

Until 1931 free trade and *laissez-faire* governed the national policy in both commerce and agriculture. They were abandoned only under the stress of the slump in food and other prices which then came upon the whole world. They were replaced by a succession of opportunist and uncorrelated measures to rescue from complete ruin first one and then another branch of arable and livestock farming. These sops to an industry thirsty almost unto death were given as subsidies, grants, quotas, and duties which were accepted by the consumer readily enough when their incidence was hidden by the falling prices of the commodities which they concerned; but which were received with some hostility when the additions they made to the cost of living became apparent in times of rising price. It could hardly have been otherwise when millions were starving on the dole. The national policy, as it was generally conceived, must be directed towards the end of balancing imports against exports; and the scope for agricultural relief on any adequate scale was therefore absent. It could hardly be present in a state of affairs in which commercial prosperity was the major aim of national life, in which there were vast surpluses of otherwise unsaleable food overseas, and in which the costs of production of food at home were so much higher than those at which it could be bought from abroad. The real competitor of the farmer was the manufacturer of goods for export. It would need a revolution in popular thought, another world war, or the disappearance of world food surpluses to restore British agriculture to full partnership in the economic life of the nation. It could never be otherwise anything but a poor relation maintained at or about the poverty line because it might at some time be able to render some service, but which must at no time pretend to full equality with the aristocrats of commerce and industry. 'Nothing would be more unfortunate,' wrote Astor and Rowntree in 1938, 'than the development of a situation in which their sectional interests [the farmers'] were placed in sharp conflict with both the national interests of the community as a whole and the central objectives of national policy.' Agriculture had to contend with the unexpressed but most formidable opposition of the vested interests which could influence government policy so strongly—the manufacturers for export, the shipping companies who flourished on cargoes of food, and the financiers who had in some way or other to collect the dividends on their foreign investments. A quarter of a century was to pass before the words of the Liberal Land Committee report of 1925 stood revealed as true, 'a nation relying only on its manufacturing industries is unstable'; or, as Dr. Cloudesley Brereton put it just before the shadows of war were beginning to loom on the horizon again, 'it is useless to be armed to the teeth if our molars have nothing to chew on'. In the meantime the attitude of the state was that of which Col. Walter Elliot has recently written. When he was Minister of Agriculture from 1932 to 1936 'at the end of day the question I always had to meet about any special consideration for home agriculture was "But will it hurt trade, will it hurt the ships?"'

In the 1920's and early 1930's it would have been a matter of little or no concern to many Englishmen or Welshmen if agriculture had ceased altogether in Britain and the land was put down to parks, football pitches and golf courses: a Scotsman might have cared. Dr. C. S. Orwin, in a remarkable and prophetic little book on *The Future of Farming*, wrote that agriculture had reached the point at which it was of no vital significance for the greater part of the people. Indeed, the popular conception of the countryman remained one in which he was seen as a rather stupid fellow whose resistance to progress had brought about his own decayed condition. The man on the land had once been highly regarded as the stable element in a restless society, but time had seemed to pass him by.

The argument that virile country folk in large numbers are necessary to the stability and vigour of the nation is, if not as old as the hills, at any rate as ancient as the first great movement of people from the land to the towns in late medieval times. It was perhaps then valid. The reasoning has been refurbished and reiterated at intervals ever since, and rarely more strongly than by the sociologists of the first four decades of the twentieth century. It has been the permanent basis of a return-to-the-land campaign in which, perhaps, the heart has sometimes ruled the head—which is not to say, of course, that instinct is no less true a guide to the eternal verities than is logic. It was peculiarly to the fore in the years between the two wars, when the suggestion was being made that the establishment of some of the millions of unemployed men upon smallholdings would not only give them a living,

but also provide the nation with a fountainhead of regenera-
tion at which to refresh and revigorate the smoke-polluted,
physically inferior, and mentally ill-balanced townsfolk.
Back-to-the-landism, even in its most stentorian mood, was
usually met by an apathetic silence or at best a lip-service
that had neither goodwill nor purpose of action behind it.
Occasionally, however, it was countered by such cogent
arguments as those assembled by the team of Astor and
Rowntree: the marks of a rising civilization are the diminishing number of people upon whom fall the burdens of producing such elementary necessities of life as food, and the
increasing number of workers in industries, professions, and
pursuits which provide those secondary amenities which turn
men from brutes into something a little lower than the gods.
By these tokens Britain had by the 1930's reached a height of
civility never before approached by mankind. On a lower,
material level it was also becoming more and more difficult
for the smallholder with little capital to compete with his
large neighbours because the field machinery which was now
essential to cheap production could not be kept at an
economic level of use even if it could be bought. Only in
livestock and its products, which need little or no mechanical
equipment, could the small farmer compete on level terms.
The advent of the tractor, the combine, the root-harvesters,
and grain-driers all tilted the scales in favour of big farming;
and the balance has come down even more decisively on
this side with every year that has passed. Sentimentality
apart, a very strong argument can be made for farming
most, if not all, of Britain in far larger farm units than
have been common for 600 years. The implications of
the mechanical revolution which has overtaken British
farming are yet hardly realized: in production of food
on factory lines, in joint stock financing of the farm, in
the economic deployment of men and machines, or in the
delegation of authority to departmental managers working

together with central pools of implements, materials, and advice. Already in the 1930's all the ingredients were being assembled.

When help for the depressed industry of agriculture came to be considered, therefore, it had to be thought of in terms applicable to the organization of farming as it was and not as some people thought it should be. The size of the contribution which agriculture could make to national defence in time of war was commonly taken as the touchstone upon which the degree of assistance to farming was judged. What sacrifice could be demanded from the consumer in peacetime to guarantee that the producer would be able to feed him in war? The amount of the bill which the nation would have to meet in order to encourage by financial means full land use was not the only factor which entered into the question, however. It was widely argued—and not even economists could say how valid was the argument—that to encourage British farming meant the restriction of food imports; that if our foreign customers could not send their grain and meat and butter here they could not pay for, and therefore could not take, the products of our industries; and that if our factories languished so would the Merchant Navy which carried Argentine grain to the Port of London and steel rails from Liverpool back to Buenos Aires. So that, if and when war came, not only would our potential armament works be decayed, but our shipping also be badly depleted. And all for having a few more acres under grain which would certainly be imported, but which could anyway be stored in strategic stores against Armageddon. Coldly presented, the reasoning did not lack force; but it was devoid of sensibility and of foresight. Just before the Second World War Britain was importing £1 million worth of food a day along trade routes of 85,000 miles over which very shortly the German submarines would be prowling for the second time in less than a generation. In Britain itself, whose granaries had been within a few weeks of complete emptiness in 1917, reserves of bread grains were no more than three months' supply. And as late as July, 1938, Neville Chamberlain, in his notorious Kettering speech, in which he maintained the supremacy of the industrial over the agricultural interest, spurned the idea of jeopardizing foreign trade by raising the output of home-grown food. It showed that Cobden still lived on, even in a prime minister of a nation which was within fourteen months to enter upon a war with a nearly empty larder.

The antagonists of agriculture were often no enemies of the farmer; but men who had the good of the land at heart, but who were persuaded that help must come from within the industry and not from without; that every husbandman must be his own Samuel Smiles. Their plea that self-help should come from the expansion of the commodities which enjoyed the natural protection of distance—in particular, milk, fruit, vegetables, and eggs—was a very reasonable one; and their suggestion that the rationalization of marketing, the improvement of quality, and the introduction of grading would do much to influence the British public in favour of home produce was accepted and acted upon.

Fundamentally, the degree of help which should be given to agriculture depended upon the conception of the place of farming in the national economy. Was it an industry among many, whose sole justification for survival was that it should fill a public need? Or did it stand apart as an integral part of Britain? The answer had lain in doubt for nearly 100 years; and except in the soon forgotten episode of the First World War the weight of public opinion had lain against the farmer. Certainly *laissez-faire* had gone in the 1930's and for that much agriculture had to be thankful. But the end of a negative policy in general did not mean that a positive policy for agriculture in particular would follow. The last thing that almost any politician wanted was to singe his fingers over agricultural assistance; for, such was the disparity between what the British farmer regarded as a fair price for his product and that at which the same commodity could be bought from abroad, assistance could come only from higher prices or higher taxation. The consumer would have to pay in either case, and the consumer was the elector. Comfort for inaction was found in the old thesis of the divison of labour, giving to each that work for which it was best fitted. Britain was the workshop of the world, and had been so for so long that her position as such was almost come to be sanctified as a divine right; and the world was Britain's larder. Indeed, so naughty and recalcitrant were some European nations in refusing to feed upon the wide acres of the American continent that the door of Britain's larder was almost the only one left open to those nations who wished to dump their foods rather than burn them. And so the farcical position arose and was maintained in which Britain, with millions of unemployed and its agriculture running at less than half-cock, was importing (in 1934) £275,300,000 worth of food and other farm produce of the type which could be grown at home.

The economists were on surer ground when they suggested that livestock and livestock products should be the primary aim of the British farmer and of such state help as could be given him. Some areas of the British Isles, particularly in the dry counties of East Anglia, are natural arable lands and well suited to grain-growing; but most of the country is, by nature of its climate, contours, or elevation, a pastoral land—but a pastoral land which can grow good cereals and roots if the nation is willing to pay for the high cost of doing so. And under intelligent and sound management, grassland which is periodically ploughed and renewed—the alternate husbandry advocated by the Cromwellian Blith and rediscovered in our own generation—under this management grassland builds up fertility against the time when an emergency demands its cropping with food crops for direct human consumption. The system of peacetime grass and wartime arable had this further advantage: the products of the pastoral farm are, many of them, those for which there exists some degree of natural or qualitative protection—from the perishable nature of milk, from the well-flavoured farm-house butters and cheeses which please the particular palate, and from prime beef and mutton from the black Aberdeen Angus and red Devons and from the sweet-fleshed sheep of the Welsh uplands and the South Downs. It may be noted in passing that part of this protection of distance and taste has now disappeared after a generation of feeding upon factory cheese, cow beef, and 'national' butter. Had the state policy of the 1930's been designed really to stimulate the production of these foods, the land would have been in better shape to meet the demands which the years after 1939 were to make upon it. Many weighty voices were being raised to this end; but conscious planning was never the distinguishing mark of the legislators of the time, and the eyes of the farming community itself were directed upon immediate palliatives rather than long-term policies. There still remained a stumbling-block, none the less important for being intangible, in the archaic conception of wheat as the staple commodity. When arable farmers took a knockout blow, the whole body of husbandmen thought of themselves as mortally wounded. In fact, in peacetime, British wheat was barely wanted. It formed a very inconsiderable part of the baker's grist, and was used mainly for biscuits and chicken-feed. But it was still popularly thought of as the very backbone of British farming, and the reluctance to jettison both ancient conceptions and ancient usages when they had outgrown their usefulness gave the townsman the grounds for yet another gibe at his rustic neighbours.

In the course of two decades of remedying first this situation

196

and then that, the state had a finger in almost every agricultural pie. By the end of the 1930's a land fertility scheme was supplying the grassland farmer with lime and fertilizers at reduced prices; a Wheat Act was guaranteeing the price of wheat to the grower, and a levy on imported grain was making good the deficiency on the price of the home-grown cereal; a subsidy on sugar beet had raised the proportion of home-grown sugar enormously; another subsidy was paid upon beef, and steps for the improvement of the animals bred included a bull-licensing scheme; and producer-controlled marketing and grading schemes were encouraging the consumption of milk, vegetables, bacon, and some minor commodities. Any one of these would have been, half a century earlier, a revolutionary interference with the internal economy of any industry, including agriculture; and taken together they made a not inconsiderable total of aid in one form or another. That they failed to reach the heart of the problem, the re-establishment of agriculture as a thriving calling which could hold up its head in the company of bankers and brewers, mill-owners, and motor car makers, was partly due to the lack of any co-ordinated, far-sighted policy behind them; and partly to the fact that the farmer was living so hand-to-mouth that the capital resources necessary to re-equip the farm for new forms of production were lacking. To produce milk cheaply and hygenically meant the building of new labour-saving cowsheds and well-equipped dairies; to grow good grass to feed meat called for a large capital investment in ploughing, fertilizers, fencing, and seeds which would be recouped slowly over several years; fruit needed the sinking of money in orchards which would pay no dividends for nearly a decade. Farming was becoming too complicated for most of its products to be as light in their demands upon capital as the cereals which grew in the field and were stored in the stack until they were sold or consumed on the farm. And once upon a time the landlord had stood behind the tenant to give him financial backing. Now the tenants were more and more being thrown back upon their own resources, which were slender after years of depression; and even had the money been there the confidence in the future to use it was not. This matter of confidence is of incalculable importance in twentieth-century agriculture. The rate of capital investment in farming grows with every new development; but policies change with governments, or even with the same government; a bright future in 1920 becomes a desolate prospect in 1921. The root cause was that farming was ultimately at the mercy of the whims of urban electors who did not understand it, or were hostile to it, or just forgot it.

The almost complete recession of the agricultural landlord as the banker and backer of the land was sufficiently realized to keep the question of land nationalization in the public mind. That the recession was on the whole an involuntary one was usually overlooked. The critic of the landlord forgot that since 1870 rents had gone steadily down, except for a small rise at the end of the First World War, but that the costs of estate maintenance had nearly doubled. Only the capital value of land had appreciated by the late 1930's, but that was largely irrelevant because to realize it the landlord had to sell his estate and cease to be a landlord. The figures of rents are instructive. In the period 1870-6 when rents averaged about 29s. 8d. an acre, aggregate farm incomes were £174 million; at the end of the First World War, with rents at 24s. 8d., farm incomes were £327 million; and in 1935-9, with rents at 19s., incomes were £169 million. The landlord had also lost a considerable measure of control over his estate except for the sporting rights. An advertisement such as that which appeared in *Farmer and Stock-Breeder* in October, 1924, might be exceptional: 'Good Hampshire farm to let . . . a tenant is required who will not interfere with the landlord's shooting.' But when a care for sporting rights exceeded the concern for the welfare of the farm, the situation played into the hands of the landlords' enemies, who retorted that the land itself was crying out for landlords who would not interfere with the tenants' cultivations and crops. The bad tenant, and others too, could once have been dispossessed arbitrarily and without financial compensation. Now a succession of agricultural holdings Acts had given the tenant a far higher degree of security, with compensation if he was disturbed in the peaceful possession of his tenure. Only in cases of bad husbandry could the tenant be given notice to quit without compensation following, but the certificate which allowed this step to be taken was granted charily by the county agricultural committees. It may be noted in passing that even the degree of security which this system gave was often questioned for its effect in shielding the bad tenant, and the opinion was widely held that the Acts had gone rather too far in this direction. Today they have gone far further. This rise in the tenants' power in the agricultural partnership was due both to the numerical superiority of the tenantry and the influence they could bring to bear upon the legislators, and to the ancient hostility to and suspicion of the landed class which began at least as early as the days of the corn law repeal agitation. And, finally, the landlord often crippled himself by attempting to maintain his estate intact when death duties had to be paid, instead of selling part of it to meet the duties and leaving his rate of capital reserves upon the rest unchanged.

The effect of all this was to replace the landlord's part in the farming enterprise by state aid. Improvements were done with the help of grant instead of by the owner. Rents were fixed and relief was given, not by rent rebates or corn rents, but by national subsidies. It was argued, and there was force behind the argument, that the landlord was taking what profits there were from his estate and leaving the maintenance to the state. What justification was there, therefore, for leaving the land in private ownership? If the state were the landlord the money which it was spending in improvements would be spent upon the betterment of its own property. As it was, every pound that the nation gave to the farmer was an indirect gift to the landlord, because it enabled the tenant to pay him a rent which he otherwise could not have afforded. Ricardo had said many years before that it was the price of produce that fixed the rent.

Land nationalization received some influential support from Dr. C. S. Orwin, from Sir Daniel Hall, and from many others. The dictum of John Stuart Mill was recalled, that 'the reasons which form the justification of private property in land are valid in so far as the proprietor of the land is its improver'. The Liberal Land Committee returned to medieval lines of thought and demanded that 'the obligation of service in return for the use of land must be reasserted so that those who hold land shall hold it as trustees . . . and that those who fail to carry out the obligations of the trust shall forfeit their trusteeship'. And they asserted that because the landlord was no longer able or willing to give farming the capital backing it needed for full efficiency, he failed in his trust and must go. There was, of course, in theory no absolute ownership of land, but only tenure in fee simple from the Crown. The Liberal argument was therefore an ingenious one. Land had originally been granted by the Crown in return for services to be rendered. The service was the *raison d'être* of the grant. Much that was both relevant and irrelevant had come in since to obscure this simple equation between tenure and the discharge of obligations; but none of it had altered the basis of the arrangement. It was now patent that the tenant-in-chief who had become *de facto* the landlord was no longer able to give the modern equivalent of the medieval services; and it was therefore just that his tenure should be terminated. The stuff of this reasoning was too full of holes to pass examination; but it surrounded the modern device of nationalization with an odour of ancient respectability. That the step of land nationalization was not in fact taken was partly due to the enormous cost of the operation, and partly to the public distrust of bureaucratic control. It would also have been a decisive step; and whatever else the years of the 1930's were they were not years of decision.

The argument, however, went on. It became more and more evident as the 1930's progressed that random palliatives were not enough to cure the deep-seated sickness of British agriculture; and two men in particular were urging the fundamental replanning of the framework of the industry. Sir Daniel Hall, as an eminent agricultural scientist and administrator, and Dr. C. S. Orwin from the great depth of his knowledge as a farm economist, historian, and agent, both propounded basically similar schemes which revolved around the nationalization of land ownership. Hall looked at the dereliction of the landlord; at that great human tragedy of modern British farming, the large army of intelligent and trained farmers in embryo who can rarely become farmers in fact for sheer lack of capital; at the uneconomic size of most British holdings; and at the considerable number of competent men who were finding their abilities restricted by too small a farm, men who were doing 300 acres well and who could manage 1,000 even better. The British farmer, he believed, was by and large no better and no worse than his opposite number in industry. It was the system which was wrong. Farming with the new scientific knowledge and with the new machines was being conducted within the stifling bounds of a system which had grown out of the medieval unit of self-subsistence. The remedies that were being applied kept the ancient framework in being, rather than encouraged the establishment of a new one, and in the end reached the pockets of the landlords as unearned and un-deserved increments upon an investment which not they but the state was making. He proposed to substitute for the now passive private landowner an active landlord in the person of the nation. The state, having acquired the agricultural land of Britain with fair compensation to the old owners, should replan it and let it to approved practising farmers working either with their own capital or with funds provided by joint stock companies of the type that had made such highly successful and productive concerns of colonial plantations. Production from this state-owned but farmer-farmed estate should be dictated by a supply board which would co-ordinate the growing of food at home with imports.

Dr. Orwin set out with the same premises and followed much the same line of argument as Hall, adding to it even greater emphasis that land improvement grants were ex-pending public money upon the betterment of private estates, and that landlords were holding society to ransom for land which was needed for development for public purposes. Both decried the back-to-the-land movement, now losing some of its force anyway, as a denial of the truism that the fewer people who are producing the necessities of life and the more who are making the luxuries the higher the degree of national civilization.

Nationalization, then as now, had a sectarian ring about it; but these proposals, whatever their merits, had no political taint about them, and were merely the well-considered ideas of men with a lifetime of agricultural experience behind them. Their schemes were overtaken and swamped by the exigencies of war and the necessities of an arid peace. But their influence is seen in the formation of the agricultural land commission for dealing with areas of particular agrarian difficulty, and in the legislation which accepted and executed Dr. Orwin's thesis that development increments upon land shall not accrue to the owner, and that land is a strictly limited national asset to be used for public and not private good.

The shortage of capital in agriculture which was a result of the growing financial difficulties of the landlord, and to the cure of which nationalization was directed, was further accentuated by the purchase by many tenants of their farms after the First World War. Times were then good, and prosperity seemed to be stabilized by legislation. Income was to spare for mortgage repayments. Landlords were getting out of their estates at the high prices then current; and purchase by the tenant was often the only alternative to dispossession. But the recession which followed the repeal of the Agriculture Act badly hit the man who had had to buy his land when it was put up for sale rather than face the alternative of losing his holding and his means of livelihood. The debts of purchase hung like a millstone around the necks of thousands of new owner-occupiers; and these mortgage debts were heavy because profits had been running high, there was keen competition for farms, and farm prices soared to fantastic heights. Landowners who sold their estates and reinvested the proceeds were able to double their incomes, because rents had been stabilized during the war and prices slumped before they were freed again for adjustment to the rate of wartime profits. In all, perhaps a quarter of the whole agricultural land of Britain changed hands in three or four years. And the result was a remarkable reversion to the seventeenth century, when in similar circumstances of financial embarrassment the late Tudor and early Stuart aristocracy had disburdened itself of its estates. The ratio of non-farming owners and owner-occupiers reached about three to one at the end of the First World War and about two to one by 1927. But never was Arthur Young's dictum that 'the magic of property turns sand into gold' more abundantly refuted than during these years, when adversity and a high proportion of owner-occupation marched together. The abdication of the landlord led perhaps to more neglect than any other factor of the time; and although the stars in their economic courses had worked against him, it was essentially his own neglect of the duties which justified his occupation of his high position which had forced the abandonment of his connection with the land. There were many and honourable exceptions, but by and large he had planned for financial safety and the maintenance of the *status quo* in a state of society which demanded rather a fine adaptability of mind and a flexibility of action.

If time had dealt unkindly with the landlord and only a little less hard with the tenant farmer, it had looked with some compassion upon the farm labourer. The exodus from the land had caused a comparative, if not an absolute, scarcity of labour; and had placed a weighty weapon of bargaining in the hands of those who remained. Food was cheap and subject to none of the old fluctuations in price. Depression still brought unemployment; but in normal times the dissatisfied farm worker could often leave the land and become gardener to a commuter, or an unskilled garage hand, or travel by bus or bicycle daily to an urban job. The old unwalled prison of the countryside had gone. That the rural depopulation was so large was partly the fault of the farm employer, partly an outcome of national policy. The comparative neglect of agriculture by the state had left the farmer in no position to pay wages large enough to keep men on the land; and the farm opposition of the past to schemes for returning to the wage-earner something of his old independence had meant that the intangible weight of the few acres which would have tipped the scale in favour of a man's remaining on the land was absent. The best men went because there was little to keep them; and those who might have supplied the incentive for them to remain grumbled and either would not learn their lesson, or having learnt it were in no position to apply it.

In 1936 the average weekly wage of the farm labourer was 32*s.* 4*d.*, below half that of a bricklayer, who was a man of less various skill than his own. Only a certain scarcity value and the pressure of his now strong union made his position as happy as it was. If there was little monetary inducement to keep a man and his family in the country, there was none of any other sort. A new generation was beginning, reasonably, to demand decent houses, water from a tap, buses into town, an accessible and comfortable school, electric light. The man of moderate means may enjoy his orderly village garden or look from his spacious window upon the country scenes outside, and thank God for a rural home. But to the working man, a leafy lane and the song of the birds were poor recompense for streaming walls and the sight of his children off on their two-mile walk in the rain to school. There was little wonder that he severed his rural roots. No sufficient effort had been made to keep the man of ambition, initiative, energy, and intelligence on the land. Of the young entry that remained, a school medical inspector wrote in 1923 of the Devon boys and girls that they were pale-faced, anaemic-looking, with eyes lacking lustre, undersized, underfed, and sad-faced.

There were in the period many prophets, and most of them were prophets of gloom. For most part the salvationists saw nationalization as the path to agrarian paradise. Among those who pinned their faith to an economic rather than a tenurial approach to the central problem of bringing prosperity back to the land were the Rural Reconstruction Association, who in 1936 put forward a plan for 'the revival of agriculture' that was a remarkable forecast of the shape of things to come. It appeared to the Association to be equitable that the British farmer should have the first claim upon his home market for the produce he could grow and sell at a fair price; which called for the regulation of imports at a level which supplemented but did not compete with British farm production. It also called for some control of home production so that it should be adjusted as closely as possible to the demand, and so obviate surpluses which undermined the market. This in turn, and also the need to ensure an equitable return for the British farmer, involved the introduction of a standard price system. This standard price should be fixed by an authority representing the producers, the consumers, and the government at a level which remunerated the farmer for his work and enabled him to pay a fair wage to his men; but which also, by a corollary of the regulation of distributors' margins, brought the food to the public at a reasonable figure. This standard price should, again, be fixed for such a number of years ahead as enabled the farmer to plan his cropping and stocking over the lengthy period of the agricultural cycle of livestock breeding policy and arable rotations; and it should be used as an incentive or discouragement in the production of commodities which became too scarce or too plentiful. To bring this plan of economic reconstruction into being and to keep it running until it found its own feet might need the application of state subsidies, but these should be used as temporary expedients and not as a permanent part of the system. In all this the Association were often only correlating advanced and informed opinion, but the synthesis was new; and the similarities between their plan and the Agriculture Act of 1947 are many and remarkable.

It is strange to remember that as recently as the beginning of the Second World War even some of the leaders of impartial agricultural thought were asking, not only whether farm production should be raised, or whether British farming could make any significant contribution to defence, but even whether it was worth farming the land of Britain at all.

Should it not become a vast playground for the towns? Neville Chamberlain, expressing at Kettering the outlook of his Midland industrial forebears, had some strange bed-fellows in the realm of economic theory. It is equally strange to think that, almost alone of all men, it was a Liberal, Baron de Forest, who as early as 1912 prophesied that the area of untilled but tillable land in the world would come to an end soon, that Britain would not be able to depend for much longer on cheap imported wheat, and that the competition of the wide acres of the New World must cease. Far nearer in time to Britain's present condition, an anonymous correspondent of *The Countryman* in 1940 forecast that after the war Britain would be too impoverished to buy enough food, and that all land would have to be cultivated right to the roadside in order to reduce the nation's adverse trade balance.

The productivity of British agriculture on the eve of the Second World War is not easy to assess. In 1937-8 the gross output was about £265 million, but this was by no means the net product of the land of Britain. At least £65 million of it was the result of processing, in farm stock, the imported feeding-stuffs; and in addition, direct and indirect financial aid from the State was going into the industry at the rate of some £40 million a year. Farm incomes were far from princely, but they rose above the losses or the meagre profits of earlier inter-war years. They averaged perhaps £1 an acre over the whole country, which gave the medium-sized farmer of 300 acres £300 a year, which included both the wages for his own labour and management and the dividend upon his capital investment of about £3,000. But as a result of the recession of agriculture from the vanguard of the nation's occupations its total contribution to the national income fell steadily. King's figures of 1688 showed that farm earnings contributed about 47 per cent. to the gross income of England and Wales; in 1867-9, when farming was

at the peak of its Victorian productivity, the percentage had
fallen to 17; in 1935-9, on the eve of the Second World War,
it was only 3·2.

The war came in 1939 as the convulsive end of an epoch.
History may see the months of 1939-40 as the moments in
time when British agriculture emerged out of the ancient
system of farming for a profit and passed into an era of farming for national subsistence which stretches in front of us as
far as the mind can reach. The permanence of the change
was obscured by the exigencies of war. It was widely
assumed that the conditions of the 1930's would return after
the fighting ended, but a few wiser heads were already
beginning to plan to give a security to post-war agriculture
such as it had not known in peace time for a century.

For the moment, however, it was necessary to concentrate
on production of food at any cost, and the Government were
advised by the nutritional experts to direct the effort at
home to providing the nation with the energy-producing
and protective foods. This meant that as much as possible
of the land of Britain which had once been under the plough
but which had fallen back to grass must again be ploughed
up to grow wheat and potatoes and sugar beet; that the
milch cow must have first call on such home-grown feeds as
barley, oats, and the good green or conserved grasses;
and that the vitamin deficiencies which would follow the
curtailment of the supplies of butter and citrus fruits must be
made good with vegetables. Beef beast, sheep and pigs had
to be greatly reduced in numbers, and carcase and processed
meat was imported instead. All these steps had to be taken so
that the public's food, and therefore the public's morale,
would survive the scarcity of imported food which might—
and did—follow both losses of ships through submarine
and aerial attack and the diversion of the bottoms of the
Merchant Navy to the carriage of troops and the munitions
of war.

As a result of the ploughing campaign, the arable land of Britain increased from 11½ million acres to 18¾ million acres by 1944, and the proportion of home-grown and imported foods was radically changed. Of the pre-war consumption of wheat and flour of 6,361,000 tons only 12 per cent. had been grown in British fields; in 1944 39 per cent. of the usage of 6,414,000 tons was home-grown. Milk for human consumption, all produced from British herds, rose from 4,609,000 tons to 6,238,000 tons. Where the nation had been growing 94 per cent. of its consumption of 3,308,000 tons of potatoes before the war, it was itself now producing 6,159,000 tons. The emphasis on bread grains, milk, and potatoes which, with fats and vegetables, were looked to to produce a basic human maintenance ration—and the success which attended the campaigns for their production—had the happy result that where a citizen had eaten 210 lb. of grain products in a pre-war year he had in 1944 252 lb.; where he had had 176 lb. of potatoes he now had 274 lb.; and where he had had 38 lb. of milk solids (excluding those in the form of butter) he now had 49 lb. Thanks to the revival of the land, the food was there for him to eat, and the full employment of wartime was giving him the money to buy it with.

Figures are wearisome things, but these have had to be given to show what British acres can do when they are given the chance; and they illuminate two aspects of wartime farming which are very pertinent to the present theme: the revelation of the degree of national self-sufficiency of which the land is capable; and the evolution of a conception of the importance of the land to the nation—which was anything but new, but which had been forgotten except for one brief interval for at least a century. The statistics of production which have been quoted are impressive, and they are the more so in that they were wrung out of a soil and an industry so inert from neglect that they could not immediately

o   209

respond to the demands made upon them. Food production from the land was a crescendo from a pianissimo opening rather than a sudden and immediate surge of brass. Many thousands of acres in Britain had been declining into infertility because so much had had to be taken out of them to make their masters' living, and the living had been so poor a one as to preclude the return of the stolen fertility from the fertilizer bag or the muck-heap. In many counties the ploughing campaign impinged upon a pastoral farming which not only had no tools for the new task, but which had forgotten how to set about it, and had not the men to do it anyway. In time all this was overcome, by the educational work of the war agricultural executive committees which were set up on the pattern of the First World War, by the financial encouragement of full fertilizer use, by the provision of implements and tractors by lease-lend, and by bringing the women of Britain back into the field—not this time in miserable amoral gangs or as starving labourers' wives and daughters, but as a land army of cheerful, vigorous, and amazingly competent young women from the towns.

The figures of production were impressive. But the result of an infinity of effort was that Britain's farming raised its contribution to the nation's food supply from 30 to 40 per cent., considered in terms of units of nutrition. The upper limit of production was certainly not reached for a variety of causes. But it may have been approached sufficiently closely to suggest that a highly populated, industrial Britain could not expect to be fed from its own acres—or at least until science comes further to the aid of intensity of production, or while the nation demands the standard of living to which it has become accustomed.

It is too early yet to tell whether the men and women of Britain are now standing in a new mental relationship to their land and their oldest industry as a result of the six years of the Second World War. The physical relationship evolved during these years was certainly a return to the eighteenth and all earlier centuries. The farmer came forward to play his new wartime role, that of an agent of the state managing under its precise instructions that part of its land which he held in his care. The nature and extent of the crops to be grown were dictated by central authority. The number and type of livestock which was kept was controlled by a careful allocation of feeding-stuffs. The farmer's rewards were based upon his known costs of production, and these costs were in turn adjusted by controlling the prices of his labour and his raw materials. And, not least important, many of the acres which had gone out of production for a variety of reasons were brought back into use by state effort and at state expense.

In the war years, from 1939 to 1945, the land of Britain was largely farmed by the state so that the nation might survive. The automobile manufacturer had made his motor cars to sell to whom and where he could; now he made tanks for the nation, under national direction and with national remuneration. The farmer had grown meat and grain and milk and wool to sell to whom and where he could; he also now grew them for the nation, under national direction and with national remuneration. State control was imposed upon the production of the state's needs, whether they came from the factory or the field. When the end of the war came no more tanks were needed; and the motor car manufacturer was permitted to return to his private enterprises. But agriculture remains in substance where it has been since 1939 because both food and the money to buy it elsewhere are scarce. And, while motor cars are desirable and valuable additions to the export trade, food is vital. The men and women of Britain must have it or starve. Farming still remains as a nominally private enterprise; but it is so hedged around with regulation and control, financial jugglery, and political expediency and exhortation, that the degree of individual action is strictly circumscribed, and its real freedom is small. And however much lip-service is paid to the cause of agrarian freedom, it may be that the man who gets his living from the land suspects in his heart that control means a reasonable prosperity but that liberty may mean liberty to starve again.[1]

[1] The final paragraph of this chapter was written before the abandonment in 1953 of many agricultural controls. I leave it unchanged because the outcome of the new policy is not yet plainly to be seen.

CHAPTER NINE

Farming for
National Subsistence

THE PRESENT may be a time of greater importance in the agricultural history of Britain than any previous period. In fifteen hundred years the farming of this island has passed through the stages of food growing for the subsistence of the grower; of agriculture which changed from self-subsistence farming to farming for profit against a background of growing social dignity based upon land ownership; and of the eclipse of the landlord and the degradation of the husbandman into national superfluity in a world of plenty. The world of plenty was, of course, an illusion. Food surpluses

213

marched with want, and grain and meat went abegging
because hundreds of millions of starving men and women in
the five continents could not afford to buy them, cheap as
they were. The redundancy of British agriculture was also
an illusion which it took a second World War to expose.
Now, for a variety of reasons which will appear later, a world
surplus is turning into a world deficit of food; and the British
farmer is looked to to feed his own people from his own
resources. The legislation and the unprecedented monetary
and technical aid for farming, which seek to cope with a
situation without parallel for several centuries, have flowed
from the nation's necessity. It seems possible that they also
arise in part from a national change of heart over the
land.

The foundations of the superstructure of statute and
subsidy that has been devised to support farming in prosperity and efficiency are the Agriculture Act of 1947. It is an
Act which is as remarkable for the duties which it imposes
upon the community of the land as for the privileges which
it gives them; and as such it is a return to a medieval conception—of fair price, of rights which are consequent upon
the performance of services—which has been newly formulated by an impersonal but increasingly paternal state in the
ancient abdication of an omnicompetent Church. It is easy
to dismiss the public opinion which has made the Act and its
corollaries possible as the consequence of the nation's having
learnt the lessons of two wars. That may be the immediate,
superficial explanation; but the basic reason may run deeper,
in a new and fundamental conception of the purpose and
place of the land. The Church forsook its practical oversight
of the social economy of the nation many centuries ago. It
has more recently, and more involuntarily, lost its ancient
hold over the minds of the majority of men; and by so doing
has left a spiritual gap. At one time it seemed as though
materialism would fill the void left by the recession of a

deistic religion. More recently there has appeared a new competitor for the veneration of man in a renaissance of the archaic fertility cult, not now of Priapus, but of John Barleycorn and Demeter. The solitude and filth, the horror and the spiritual starvation of a nation in arms in foreign lands confirmed—for good or ill—the replacement of the Cross by the plough as the principal of the *lares et penates* upon many a personal altar. The universal purpose, if there be any, is seen to be working in seed-time and harvest, and not through a vicarious redemption of the sins of mankind; and salvation is sought, not with the knees upon a hassock and the eyes upon a celestial heaven, but with the hands upon a tractor wheel and the eyes upon the furrow slice turning from the mouldboard of the plough. The priests are clad not in surplice and cassock, but in the overalls and the gumboots that have replaced fustian homespun in the field.

This twentieth-century phenomenon is very, very far from universal. It is often the outward manifestation of an inward sentimentality which is as transitory as it is deplorable. But it is possible that it is a significant element in the public support for the legislative encouragement of an agricultural renaissance. This encouragement, which is embodied in the machinery which the Agriculture Act set up to regulate prices and markets for 'such part of the nation's food and other agricultural produce as it is desirable in the national interest to produce in the United Kingdom'—an elastic definition, be it noted, which may be expanded or contracted at will—was in effect a non-party measure which consolidated the ideas formulated by the government, the farmers' unions, and the workers' and landowners' organizations during and after the war. It regulates the fortunes of agriculture to a degree never before approached in peacetime; but the nation, and its farmers among it, are now well enough inured to such regulation in most spheres of life not only to accept it, but even to fight against its repeal.

A remarkable *quid pro quo*, to the medieval origin of which reference has already been made, is the hallmark of the Act. The prices to be paid for farm produce by the Ministry of Food are determined at an annual review of the national economic atmosphere, the nation's need for one food as against another, and the average costs of production, all considered against a preceptual background of good husbandry. Where, as in livestock husbandry, plans for development have to be laid well in advance, prices are fixed for a period of years ahead. In effect, the national farm is conducted on a cost-plus basis. In return for an unprecedented stability, agriculture has given hostages to fortune in the shape of acquiescence in a statutory requirement that it shall discipline itself into a universal efficiency: the farmer by threat of dispossession by his peers on the county executive committee if he should fail to make reasonably good use of his holding, the landlord by threat of dispossession of his estate if he neglects to keep it properly equipped for farming.

The Act was welcomed as a milestone along the road to agricultural prosperity and to a proper equilibrium between the farmer, the land, and the state; which it undoubtedly is. It is in the agricultural interest that the integrity of the Act should be maintained. But second thoughts, honestly held and with some justification, have already questioned the wisdom of some of its parts. Prices are fixed in relation to the costs of production of the commodities which the nation needs; and farming is thereby insulated from the hazards of world prices and the keener aspects of competition under the laws of supply and demand to an extent not enjoyed by any other industry. Has agriculture an intrinsic right to such unusual treatment; to a high degree of protection against overseas supplies and the vicissitudes of international commerce; to the enjoyment of a unique buffer between itself and the cold winds of fortune? Again, prices are fixed on a basis of average costs of production. The process inevitably means that the highly efficient farmer or the man who has an unusual fertility of soil or convenience of holding receives a disproportionately high reward. Is the incidence of taxation sufficient to bring his net income into line with his less fortunate or less intelligent fellows? Has the Act, by guaranteeing a living to the average man, removed the incentive to farm well? These are all pertinent questions which cannot be brushed aside, however confirmed one is in the belief that agriculture is a fundamental occupation which should be taken outside the realm of party politics and the cut and thrust of ordinary commerce.

There are no less doubts about the machinery of self-discipline within the industry which the Act devised to maintain efficiency in an occupation from which the sharp steel of competition has been removed. In this matter of a patently fair return by agriculture, in the shape of universal efficiency, for the manifold benefits conferred upon it may lie the key to the future of farming. Agriculture has been given state protection, but has been allowed to regulate its own state of health, and to decide which of its own limbs are too useless to be kept. The industry, open to the gaze and the judgement of all who pass by its fields, is sensitive to criticism. But its members are kindly men who will stand up for one of themselves against the world. There are doubts, whether they be well founded or not, whether farmer members of county executive committees, upon whom rests the responsibility for taking the first steps towards the dispossession of the inefficient, are not sheltering too many of their fellows who are incompetent, lazy, or ignorant. Agriculture has no higher proportion of these than any other industry; but no other industry enjoys the particular protection against adversity of the farmer, with whom economic natural selection has largely ceased to operate; no other industry is so wide open to the public view for all to see and judge; and no other industry has so many men outside it who consider themselves to be knowledgeable and competent critics.

Upon a broader basis, it is also being suggested that the Agriculture Act is fixing the framework of farming at a time when rapid advances in the ancillary sciences are requiring the reshaping of field and farm boundaries and, perhaps, a regional differentiation of production.

The Agriculture Act has conferred another boon upon farming by giving a security of tenure so strong as to amount in effect to a lease for life at a fixed rent. The impact of this provision upon the ancient relationship of landlord and tenant may most conveniently be discussed in connexion with the continued decay of the system of the landed estate in private ownership; it is noted here to round off the list of benefits which this Act has provided for the man in immediate physical control of the land of Britain. A further point may be added. The initiation of the Act and the working of its price-fixing mechanism would have been either far more difficult or even impossible in the absence of strong farmers' unions, led numerically, and perhaps intellectually, by the National Farmers' Union of England and Wales. This body originated and operated in a small way before the First World War, gathered members and strength in the interval between the wars, and has consolidated its position as the only spokesman, outside the technical Press, of the working farmer since 1939. It now controls the destinies of everyday agriculture and the shaping of national policy to a remarkable degree, and it is a tribute to the wise leadership at its head that in general it has steered the industry in a statesmanlike and responsible way, with an eye to national needs unusual in an organization with purely sectional interests and a membership of the most individualistic body of men in the world. It speaks for farming in the councils of the nation; and not the least valuable part of its work has been the substitution of sound argument backed by valid statistics for the ancient rural rhetoric as a weapon of negotiation and information.

This, then, is one of the factors which is shaping the post-war pattern of British farming: an Act which has given the farmer secure prices, markets, and tenures in return for the exercise of a reasonable degree of efficiency in his calling. The second, and international factor, is as new as it is incalculable. The quantity of food grown upon the cultivated lands of the world has not varied considerably since pre-war days. There were then large food surpluses, which were surpluses not because the food was not wanted for human nutrition, but because the larger part of the people of the world could not afford to buy it. World population is increasing fast. It is (1952) of the order of 2,400 million people. There will be 20 million more next year. There must be added to the mere numerical increase in the mouths to be fed a general world-wide rise in purchasing power and a greater sense of governmental responsibility for the feeding of the peoples. The world surplus has turned at best into an equilibrium, and at the worst perhaps into a deficit. This state of affairs had long been foreseen by a handful of prophets, but not apparently by any statesman of influence. Malthus forecast it in 1798, and his fears would have come true half a century ago had the true situation not been temporarily hidden by the exploitation of the new American and other sources of food. By 1898 Sir William Crookes was telling the British Association that the readily tillable new lands of the world had nearly all been brought into use. And de Forest in 1912 said that the time would not be far distant when American and other surpluses would cease from troubling the farmers of Britain. Indeed, against the background of world nutrition, the rapid and great expansion of American food production may be seen not as the enemy of the prosperity of the British farmer, but as a fortunate accident which maintained for a little time longer a universal balance between supply and demand.

It is quite impossible to determine the true facts of the present international position. On the one hand, the world population is said to be outrunning the world's potential supply of food at an alarming rate. The result must be world-wide starvation, which is Nature's method of restoring the *status quo*. It can be avoided only by a neo-Malthusian limitation of population, especially among the rapidly increasing nations of the East, from whom modern science has removed many of the old death-dealing ways of maintaining a balance. On the other hand, it is categorically stated that the world has sufficient resources to give an adequate diet to everyone everywhere; and that the solution lies not in limiting population, but rather in increasing the production of food to the limit of which the agricultural land of the world is capable. Each school of thought has adherents who are better placed than most men for knowing the facts. Fortunately, it is not necessary for the present purpose to seek to resolve the difference. It is necessary merely to make the point that British agriculture is, at the moment, being conducted against a world background in which a permanent, substantial overseas competition such as existed before 1939 is improbable, in the immediate future and for the main commodities at least. The British farmer of this generation can reasonably look forward to having his own market in his own hands without fear of dumping or undercutting.

There is, therefore, the statutory machinery for enabling the British farmer to plan ahead with some confidence; and a world situation which would seem to reinforce the statutory guarantees of market and price which he has been given. What more? The threat to Britain's financial stability has arisen since the war because of the encashment of our foreign investments to pay for the fight; and also because of the growing industrialization of our old customers, who are not only now making the goods they once bought from Britain, but also capturing some of our pre-war markets for themselves. Foreign food is, therefore, not coming in in payment for our exported commodities at anything like the pre-war rate; nor, if we are honest with ourselves, is it likely to do so in the foreseeable future. An industrial and commercial honeymoon of more than a century is over, and the British nation has got to start housekeeping for itself once more. In spite of the pious hopes of the politicians and of temporary ameliorations in the terms of trade, matters seem likely to get worse, not better. To retrieve our pre-war position in the world's markets, it would be necessary for us to expand our pre-war rate of exports by three-quarters, which appears to be a sheer impossibility in the face of competition far fiercer than in the past. The corollary of all this is obvious. Food cannot be imported; therefore it must be grown at home and with as little reliance upon foreign aids in feeding-stuffs, fertilizers, and machines as possible. The process will absorb into agriculture more capital; and the economist is loath to accept this condition, because the money would earn more wealth in industrial cash or credits— which make a poor meal for a starving nation—than in farming, which provides one of the two absolute needs of mankind, food and air. But the world and our own condition will not let us go on living as we have done in the past.

With these premises in mind, the question must be faced. How far can Britain feed herself? But not just yet. There are some other factors to be considered first which concern the land itself: how it is owned, and the changes in the nature of the ownership; how far marginal land may and should be brought into full food production; the alternative claims upon land, and whether Britain can afford to sink acres under concrete and brick and water; and the place of forestry in the economy of the land. Given these facts and arguments, we should be the better able to judge the opinions that are expressed upon the central theme of both this time and this book, the place of agriculture in our society. Farming has become again what it was for so long before the industrial era, the chief weapon in the fight for national survival. Fundamentally we may be back where this long story began, looking for life itself to fertile field and busy plough. It is not, this time, a plea for a return to the land for sentimental, for cultural, or for charitable reasons; not a cosseting of the farmer as a line of wartime defence; not a regard for the soil as a living asset to be cherished both for itself and against future need; but bare, stark, frightening necessity.

First, the pattern of land ownership. The National Farm Survey of England and Wales, conducted from 1941 to 1943 by the Ministry of Agriculture, made possible the first really accurate analysis of the ratio of absentee—or, rather, non-farming—owners and owner-occupiers. It showed that 33 per cent. by area of all land under crops or grass was being farmed by the men who nominally owned it, although ultimate ownership might lie with a bank or a mortgage corporation. In East Anglia, the percentage of owner-occupiers of the normal farm of 100 to 700 acres was as high as 64 per cent. The percentage of owner-occupiers by number was 35. These figures may have changed somewhat in the decade since the survey was ended, but any movement will have been towards an extension of owner-occupation to a percentage which may now stand at 40. But the figure of non-farming owners will itself have been radically amended in its complexion by the recent rapid increase in public ownership of land. The landlord is changing fast from the ancient pattern of the country gentleman to the new fashion of a government land agent. The Forestry Commission has become the largest single landowner in the country, with more than 1½ million acres in England, Wales, and Scotland under its control. The Agricultural Land Commission manages land which has come to the state in lieu of cash for death duties, and in other ways. The county councils hold considerable areas of smallholdings and other property. The Church of England and the universities, although very great landlords, lie outside the category of public owners because the profits from their estates go to the benefit of sectional interests. All in all, the land in strictly public hands probably extends to nearly 5 million acres today (1952). In the British fashion, nationalization has been extended insidiously and without the provocation of party strife or the annoyance of the landed interests.

The National Farm Survey also made it possible for the first time to assess the true condition of the fixed equipment of the farms of England and Wales—the state of the farmhouses, the buildings, farm roads, fences, and drainage works; and to ascertain how the landlords and tenants of the country had kept their properties in repair. Some 58 per cent. of the farmhouses were in good condition, 37 per cent. in fair condition, and 5 per cent. bad. Buildings made a rather worse showing, with 39 per cent. good, 49 per cent. fair and 12 per cent. bad. Only 38 per cent. (by area) of the internal roads, fences, and ditches were good, and 45 per cent. of the field drainage. In all cases—houses, buildings, and the rest—condition has undoubtedly improved considerably in the years since the survey was made. There has been more money to sink in improvements, both from farm profits and from state grants made for this specific purpose.

The economic position of the landlord has deteriorated yearly. Rents have been stabilized by the Agriculture Act at a figure of roughly 27s. an acre for all holdings of five acres and upwards, or for the normal farm of 100 to 700 acres at about 23s. an acre. The variations between regional rents is large, from 46s. or over an acre in the Fens to less than 20s. in Brecon, Radnor, and other Welsh upland counties. Large as the variation appears, it does not even so reflect the true value of the better land to the occupier today. The Fens will certainly yield a profit per acre ten times that of the hills of Cardigan. Rents have, in effect, been fixed not very much above the depression figures of the 1930's; rent control stepped in before they were brought into line with wartime earnings; and they bear only a vague—and often very low —relationship to the value of the land to the occupier. But while rents have remained stable, the costs of estate maintenance have risen greatly; and it is commonly computed that as an immediate financial investment land is at the bottom of the national list with a net return of only 1 or 2 per cent. As a long-term investment, of course, it still gives a security equal to or even surpassing government bonds, for it is the one permanent, unchanging asset, whether of the nation or the individual.

Whether fixed rents are an unmixed blessing to the farmer is a point upon which there is much argument. Low rents —and none can deny that today rents are far below the real annual market value of the land—discourage intensity of land use. And with a standard range of prices for farm commodities over the whole country, rent differences far from level out net farm earnings: rents form a far lower proportion of the production cost of a crop on good land than on bad, and the farmer lucky enough to have soil of high natural fertility makes more than his share of the industry's total profit upon certain commodities.

The question of nationalization has faded into the background with the provision made by the Agriculture Act for requiring proper estate management by the landlord. He keeps his farms well equipped, or is dispossessed. The landowner has enjoyed large profits and immense incidental advantages in the past. Today he is a member of a downtrodden occupation; and, like the pensioner and the man living upon a fixed income from investment, he has been overtaken and nearly overwhelmed by the flood tide of rising costs. Nationalization has meant, at any time since it was first advanced as a policy, state ownership and not state farming. Today, effective control of the land has passed out of the hands of the landlord. The old reasons for state ownership have largely gone. The tenant has now been given lifelong security of tenure. Powers of compulsory purchase make it more difficult for the community to be held to ransom or mulcted by the land speculator. And farm boundaries can be adjusted for greater efficiency of land use on the advice of the Agricultural Land Commission, which also has the task of surveying areas referred to it for proposed acquisition by the state in the cause of better farming. All that is left to the harassed landlord is the administration of his estate for a low reward; and, occasionally, to extend his own farming upon holdings of which the tenancies come into hand. Even the aura of social dignity of the landed gentry is gone; and a great part of this class in the pages of *Burke* now owns no single British acre.

Land nationalization has never been entirely a party measure. It has been advocated by men of all shades of political opinion who have considered it a necessary step towards full efficiency in farming. The proportion of its supporters has, in the nature of things, been higher among the industrial, Liberal descendants of the Anti-Corn Law Whigs and among the Socialists. Even in the ranks of the Fabian 'new thinkers', however, it is apparent that Keynes's doctrine of control by fiscal means is replacing the old dogmas of the nationalization of all the means of primary production; and it is possible that Socialist aspirations may be satisfied by such agreed measures of financial and physical control as those contained in the Agriculture Act, even if the degree of monetary reward for the better exponents of the art and science of farming sometimes comes under debate. In any case, the end of state ownership seems to be coming to be reached rapidly by a natural, non-doctrinaire process of attrition.

There is, in Britain, an immense range of quality in land, agriculturally viewed. It varies from the moss-covered heights of the Scottish mountains, where as on Ben Nevis the mean annual temperature is below freezing-point, through the lower but still inhospitable peaks of the Snowdon massif to the immensely fertile silts of the Fens and the kindly loams of Kent. Of this bewildering complex about 28½ million acres are improved farmland and something more than 18 million acres are in extensive agricultural use or no use at all. Many of these 18 million acres—perhaps half of them or even more than half—are useless for all practical purposes: they are too rocky and precipitous, or the soil is too thin or altogether absent, or the climate too unkind, or there is no reasonable means of access. These areas may be dismissed from the agricultural calculation—for the present, at any rate. But the remainder—an area of unknown extent, of up to 9 or 10 million acres—is hill or marginal land with practical food-producing potentialities. Even in this restricted category the range of quality and of possibilities of use is very great. Some of the land, indeed—the marginal areas—has been in and out of cultivation or normal stocking according to the warmth or coldness of the winds of agricultural fortune. The hills of Devon and the slopes of Exmoor, for example, are lined with old, grass-grown ridge-and-furrow where the plough once went when corn-growing prospered, or when absence of transport until recent times made it necessary for the inhabitants to remain self-sufficient in their food. The marginality of these areas lies partly in the quality and depth of soil, in the altitude and climate, in the absence of means of access or convenient field layouts, cottages, or good buildings, and partly in the current degree of profit upon the food they can produce.

Some areas need only a large initial investment to bring them into full use, by the provision of buildings and roads. Others need both the first capital and an annual subsidy ever after to make it profitable for the private farmer to farm them. In the latter case, the ratio between the input of labour and fertilizers and the output of crop, as grain or meat or milk, is too close to permit of a sufficient reward to be taken from the normal range of fixed farm prices. It may cost an Exmoor farmer £20 to grow an acre of wheat worth £21, where, a Norfolk man's outlay might be £15 and his return £30.

In general, these marginal and hill lands are primarily pastoral areas, and they should be so used. Modern machinery, modern fertilizers, and modern strains of grass seeds make it possible for them to be improved far more easily and with greater assurance of success than in the past. Holdings in the desolate heart of Exmoor have had their stock-carrying capacity quadrupled by ploughing up, taking fodder crops for stock, and then seeding them down to grass leys. But the capital cost is high, at least £30 an acre, which is a very great deal of money for a hill farmer to find for work on any extensive scale. The reclamation of even 10 acres will absorb all his year's profit. The state, appreciating the size of the problem and the rewards in terms of food which financial help will bring, has already given some aid for these areas; and the money has been put to very good use indeed. Scores upon scores of holdings in the hills of the south-west, of Wales, and of the north are becoming model upland farms, great reservoirs of beef and mutton and wool, thanks to the government grants of recent years. Nowhere has the growth of enlightened self-interest on the part of the state borne greater fruit than here.

The whole question of the use of these regions of agricultural difficulty is fundamentally one of national need and national finance. Even the best of the medium-sized holdings in the hills are even now earning for their occupiers an annual income little more than that of a shorthand-typist in a city office, with none of the anxieties, hard manual labour, and considerable financial investment of the hill farmer. A case may be, and often is, made out for keeping these men on their feet and their families on their land for sociological reasons. Setting that aside for the moment, the fact remains that if the nation wants meat it is to these hills that it has to look for much of it, and it will have to pay for it. The situation is, basically, as simple as that. The alternative to state-aided, intensive use of these hill and marginal lands is an extensive dog-and-stick ranching, with one sheep to 10 acres instead of five sheep to every acre, and 5 lb. of mutton instead of 250 lb. from an acre. Here again the question is being asked whether it is equitable for state funds to be used for the improvement of private property; but to whom the bill is to be paid is a point which must be settled politically and not agriculturally.

Neither the hills of the west and north nor the lowlands of Britain to the south-east of the upland line that runs from Exeter to Newcastle are, however, being left intact for farm use. The very ancient movement of land from agricultural to urban purposes has now, by the very pressure of population upon food supplies, suddenly become a problem of the first magnitude; and it is a problem which appears likely to be accentuated rather than solved in the future. Complaints of the diversion of land from food-growing to other uses are almost as old as the rise of towns and industries. As early as 1314 'the poor men of the county of Devon' complained that the West-Country tin-miners were destroying good farm land 'including arable, wood and meadow as well as gardens and houses', at the rate of more than 300 acres a year. Through the last eight or nine centuries the towns and cities of Britain have been spreading themselves over the plough lands, meadows, and pastures around them; and none more so than London, which during the past 200 years has encroached upon and engulfed the fertile market gardens of Middlesex and recently added the appropriation for Heath

Row airport of some thousands of acres of good horti-
cultural land.

By and large, grumbling was stilled when land was either
relatively plentiful or gave a low profit. At almost any time
between 1880 and 1939 landowners were ready, indeed
eager, to sell their unprofitable estates for development, and
very glad indeed to take a cheque many times larger than that
which would have been paid them for farm land as such. The
loss of the land under brick and mortar, roads, and water was
as inherently serious then as it is now; but the permanent
gravity of the recession was obscured by the temporary superfluity of these particular acres for food production. As much
meat and grain, butter and cheese was coming into British
ports as the people could eat, or afford to eat, and what did
it matter if houses spread over the cornfields of Hertfordshire
and Essex or the pastures of Leicestershire? Planners, indeed,
were worried; but they were concerned rather over the un-
tidiness of development and ribbon building alongside the
new arterial roads than over the potential loss of food. The
objection was an aesthetic and social one rather than one of
nutrition.

A decade and a half, shortening world supplies of food,
national financial difficulties, and the greater profit to be
taken from agricultural use of land have now made the
removal of an area out of productive use a matter of very
great moment. It is computed that of the 28½ million acres
of farmed land in Britain (excluding Ulster), about 750,000
will be lost to food production in the next twenty years if the
plans now laid mature. This is equivalent in area to the whole
county of Gloucester or the East Riding of Yorkshire. The
annual loss, expressed in homely terms of food, is 2,000,000
loaves of bread, 5,300 tons of cereals, 9,500 tons of potatoes,
600 tons of sugar, 150 tons of lamb, 350 tons of pork and
bacon, 8,750,000 eggs, and 2,000,000 gallons of milk.

The apparently insuperable difficulty is that much of the

land that is being taken is really needed for other purposes; although often the requisitions are excessive and alternative areas of less agricultural value are neglected. But, by and large, it is necessary that houses should be built in uncongested areas for a population which is increasing, although more slowly than in the past, which is rightly demanding more living space than it has had in mean streets, and which does not take kindly to the obvious solution of flats that expand vertically in place of the traditional housing estates which expand laterally. Children have a right to more airy schools with playing fields which are big enough. New arterial roads must be made if traffic is not to become completely chaotic. It may be proper that factories should be built in the countryside for strategic and social reasons. Reservoirs have to be constructed and airfields laid out. It is very much more questionable whether opencast coal working is really necessary; or whether the nation cannot afford to restore to use the thousands of acres made sterile by the removal of topsoil for iron-ore mining. No sensible person can deny that many of these calls upon land are necessary, or that others of them are desirable if the citizens of Britain are to live with the amenities which they can reasonably expect. But the production of food may—and the word 'may' is advisedly used, for none can aspire to certainty in this matter—it may come to have an importance which will overwhelm all other demands; when an acre under wheat may prevent the starvation of a family. Food is one of the prime necessities of life; spacious houses, schools, playing fields, fast roads, airfields, all come lower in the list. Town and country planning Acts have been passed in plenty, and the machinery for the regulation of land use is in existence. What seems to be needed is an overriding decision upon the right balance of the national land budget. Part of the trouble may lie in the fact that wolf has been cried too often, and cases have been overstated where inconvenience of management following the

halving of farms or the loss of third-rate land for first-rate
urban needs have been magnified into national calamities.
But these cases do not detract from either the magnitude or
the gravity of the problem. The land, admittedly, is made for
man and not man for the land—at least, from the narrower,
anthropocentric point of view; but man is a thriftless being
who must be guarded against himself in many matters, and
this is one of them. The change of material values has
perhaps been too sudden for a conscious adjustment to have
yet been made, a change of conception of land as an un-
limited and unessential commodity to land as a precious
and very limited asset.

The boundary between land in agricultural and non-
agricultural use might seem to be a precise one. In fact, it is
not. The principal object that obscures the division is the
tree. Ecologically, timber is a more natural form of vegetation
than the artificial grass upon which the milch cow grazes or
the wheat that is reaped for bread. Economically, it is
distinct, for it cannot be eaten. The forest was once almost as
important as the arable clearings which were made in it by
the pioneers; for without wood there was no fuel to keep
men warm or to cook food; or, in stoneless areas, the material
to build houses; or the timber to make boats. Time has
modified the place of woodland in personal affairs; coal
is, directly or indirectly, the source of warmth; houses are
built of brick or concrete; and ships are made of steel.
Man has lost his ancient appreciation of the place of the
forest in his own little self-centred economy. Timber has
become an industrial and not an immediately personal
need. And the tree has become the enemy of many a farmer,
and a potential menace to pasture for beef beast and
sheep.

The forest cover of Britain had been clear-felled by countless generations of agricultural pioneers until by Tudor days
the countryside was largely deforested. Silviculture became

a hobby with some landlords in the eighteenth century, particularly in Scotland, where 'the planting Duke' of Atholl set 27 million trees upon his Perthshire estates, but in general little was done to renew the ancient woodland cover; and the First World War took a heavy toll of the remaining timber. The standing reserves became so small that, in 1919, the Government created the state-financed Forestry Commission to restore a reasonable degree of self-sufficiency in wood against another war. In a sphere of cropping in which a man sows for his sons to cut, it was inevitable that by 1939 still only about 4 per cent. of the timber used in Britain was home-grown. An ambitious post- (Second) war planting policy was drawn up, in which 900,000 acres are to be afforested in the first decade; and, in fact, three-quarters of the area planned has already been planted—217,600 acres out of an aim of 290,000 by 1950-1. In its thirty-three years' existence since 1919 the Forestry Commission has become, by purchase and gift, the largest landowner in the country, with 1,781,500 acres acquired up to 1951. Of this, 737,000 acres are planted, and the rest is awaiting planting or is unsuitable for forestry. Besides the 413 forests which the Commission owns, it also aids private forestry on 73,731 acres, with an equal area awaiting ratification (1951), by planting and maintenance grants.

All this is a sizeable achievement, and it has naturally not been reached without controversy and criticism of detail. These criticisms have mainly revolved around two points: the encroachment of plantations upon farm land and the species of trees planted. The former objection appears to be the weightier. There is, in the nature of things, much marginal land where it is difficult to draw a dividing line between the just claims of the tree and of the sheep. Both flourish on the leeward slopes of the hills of Wales and Scotland; and the economy of upland sheep farms has occasionally been upset by afforestation. The loss of potential food-producing land would not, however, seem to be considerable. The forests have gone up in soils, elevations and climates where little else but a tree could prosper. They have by no means always been made upon the hills. The barren wastes of Charnwood which march with some of the best Leicestershire feeding pastures, the blowing sands of the Brecklands which lie cheek by jowl with the good Norfolk barley lands, and the thin soils of the Bagshot series at London's back door are often as well suited for afforestation as the mountainsides of Ross-shire or the Snowdon foothills around Beddgelert. All in all, the work of the Forestry Commission in planning and executing one aspect of land use is a remarkable object lesson in successful state farming, but of farming for timber and not food.

It is the natural, and perhaps unavoidable corollary of state farming that mass production from centrally planned and administered regions should be stereotyped. The second criticism of the work of the Forestry Commission flows from this fact. Tidy regiments of rectangular forests march across the hills in place of the haphazard spinney and the formless relicts of the natural woodland cover. Industry asks for softwoods, and so for every beech or oak tree that is planted there are nine spruces, pines, larches, or other conifers. Unnatural, say the purists; Britain is a land of oak and ash, beech and elm and birch, but now horrid pine-trees have come in. In fact, all land use is unnatural. Mankind can live only by encouraging Nature to move along new, predetermined, and more productive lines. And if the indigenous cover must always be preferred, then so must wheat and the good grasses give place to the ancient mantle of bramble and bracken, nardus grass and sedge. The aesthetic objection appears to be equally untenable. Beauty is in the eye of the beholder; and the eye has become so accustomed to the undisciplined hedgerow and thicket, wandering lane and shapeless field that these things seem intrinsically beautiful.

Familiarity with the new forms of the countryside, whether of the precisely deployed forest or the great hedgeless fields made to fit the combine harvester, will invest them with a particular beauty of their own. It is not many centuries since the rustic reactionaries were wagging their grey beards over the disappearance of the wide landscapes of the open fields and the arrival of the new-fangled quickthorn hedges. Yet these same hedges are now the essential framework of bucolic beauty.

It has already been pointed out that agriculture is no longer a self-sufficient industry. Financially, it has not been such for many centuries. At least from Elizabethan days new capital has been steadily brought in from foreign adventure, from international commerce, from piracy, from industry; and long before that the lords of the manor financed their tenants on stock-and-land leases with cash from many sources. At no time more than the present has financial aid from without come in so abundantly to the aid of farming. But so rapidly has the capital needed to finance the land risen that more capital is more urgently needed than ever before (or, some argue, the capital already in farming needs to be redeployed and put to better uses). For longer than many people are prepared to admit, the business-man has brought good new blood into farming. He has also been a great source of new cash for the land. He is dismissed somewhat contemptuously as a hobby farmer—almost exactly four hundred years ago the preachers were inveighing against the merchants of London who 'bie fermes out of the hands of worshipfull gentlemen, honest yeoman, and pore labouring husbandes'—and as one whose interest in the land is to lose in agriculture the taxable profits he has made in industry. The latter reason is often true; but the former jibe is unmerited more often than not. The men who go into farming from business with the intention of doing an efficient job upon commercial lines are among the very best farmers that

Britain can boast. They bring into an under-capitalized and not very highly organized concern the money, the keenness of management, the business acumen, the ability to take both good advice and a risk, all of which are among the principal needs of the land today. It may not be overstating the matter unduly to say that the ancient position is being reversed, and that the towns are revivifying the countryside.

While capital came into farming from very ancient times, agriculture remained self-sufficient in its other needs for very much longer. But during the last century and a half it has had to become more and more reliant upon external supplies of the tools of its trade. In fertilizers it has become dependent upon the phosphates of North Africa, the potashes of Germany. It looks to the industrial chemist for the means of protection against crop diseases and insect pests. Most of all, its machines and implements are the products of factories, skilled technicians, and trained designers; and the sources of its power—petrol, paraffin, and diesel oil—are brought from overseas. The output of the British farm is, therefore, by no means all a clear addition to the national wealth. A thousand urban man-hours have gone into each tractor, and the tractor has also been designed and tooled for at a cost of more than £1 million. Before the tractor can move an inch, wells have had to be bored in Kuwait or Texas, the oil shipped and refined and transported to the farm. For the corrugated iron or asbestos that have replaced local timber or village-made bricks for the farm buildings, the sheep netting that is substituted for the natural hedge, the grass seeds from New Zealand that take the place of the sweepings of the hay barns, the teat cups of the milking machines that come from the rubber trees of Malaya to take the place of the horny hands of the dairyman, British farming has to depend upon national and international industry and commerce.

It is, therefore, almost impossible to relate the present output of the land of Britain to the statistics of the past. Indeed, it has been calculated that in the four immediate post-war years, a farm of high efficiency used £5 worth of imported materials and £5 worth of home-produced materials to turn out £20 worth of food an acre. And the greater the output of the farm, the more external aid there has to go into it.

This is an important matter to be borne in mind when the question is considered, against the background which has been briefly stated, how far can Britain feed herself? In 1951 the land of Britain grew, in gross, a quarter of the wheat and flour needed by the nation, nearly a quarter of the sugar, roughly half the meat and bacon, only one-twentieth of the butter and one-fifth of the cheese, seven-eighths of the shell eggs, all the liquid milk, and nearly all the potatoes. This is the position which has been reached after more than a decade of concentration upon home food production at almost any cost; and it may appear to be a disheartening measure of the distance by which the population of Britain has outrun its internal resources. The gap between mouths to feed and the domestic food to feed them on opened a century ago, and widened rapidly thereafter; but the exploitation of foreign soils has hidden it until now, and we have been living in a fools' paradise, both economically and dietetically. The ancient peasant was nourished by his bread, the ale made from one or another of his cereals, some cheese, what illicit game he could take from the chase or warren, the carcase of a sheep or beast that was past its usefulness, a little pig meat, and mighty little else. As the level of agricultural production outran the rise in population for some centuries, the nation as a whole fared better, and meat and butter, good wheaten bread and cheese were to be had in plenty by those who could pay for them. As the rise in population under the stimuli of industrial expansion and better health outran the level of home food production the sources of the New World came in to supplement the food from British fields. These sources are now cut off, and the nation with nearly 50 million mouths to feed is being forced back upon the output of the acres, somewhat extended indeed by reclamation, which gave the ancient peasant his sufficient but monotonous diet.

At the present time there is only a little more than half an acre a head to feed the people of Britain from their own land. The overwhelming importance of ensuring that every farm is well equipped and cropped, that every possible acre is kept or brought into food production, is evident. The hope for national survival lies in the fact that, as the *Observer* has recently pointed out, British farming is only beginning to face the task in front of it. The problem of the highest possible output of food from the land has many facets. The human one, where the will and the confidence to farm highly have yet to be universally implanted, and the replacement of the inherently incompetent farmer has yet to be fully and courageously tackled; the scientific one, in which the breeding of new and more productive crop varieties and the further simplification and improvement of livestock breeding by artificial insemination hold out immense promise of greater returns for the same input of labour and materials; the disseminatory one, in which the new and very important advisory services are devising wider and better ways of bringing the scientific advances of the laboratory into practice in the field; and the tenurial and financial ones upon which we have already dwelt. But when all that may be still wrong has been put right and when science has moved even further forward, it is still doubtful whether Britain can hope to be fed from its own land, at least at the high level of variety and palatibility which it has become accustomed to enjoy from the ploughlands and pastures of the world.

Official view is that it cannot; and that the maintenance of an industrial export trade at a very high level indeed is a continuing necessity. Basically, it is held, it would be possible to produce at home the bare bones of the nation's nutrition; but they would be an unappetizing skeleton of

237

bread, oatmeal, potatoes, sugar, the coarser vegetables, a little milk, a minute amount of cow beef. To do even this the plough would have to be taken into the natural grass-lands of Britain, and imports of fertilizers and animal feeding-stuffs would have to be considerable. The flesh that clothes the bones and makes them tasty—good beef, tender lamb, the rasher of bacon and the leg of pork, a well-matured Cheshire cheese, fresh eggs, creamy milk, farm butter—would all be almost or completely absent.

An alternative view comes from the Rural Reconstruction Association, who set out to determine what increases in stock and crop yields would be needed, with full land use, to produce from home agriculture all the food the nation needs and which the British farmer can grow. The list must obviously exclude such exotics as tea, coffee, and most vegetable oils; and the national need is assessed upon the sufficient but far from generous rationing scale of 1946. Upon the basis of recent farm yields some 12,820,000 acres would be needed for the production of food for direct human consumption; and 36,733,000 acres for livestock for meat, for such livestock products as eggs and milk, and for the maintenance of working horses. But there are no more than 35,530,000 acres in Great Britain and Ulster which can reasonably be used. It is therefore calculated that the deficiency would, and could, be made good by increasing production by about 40 per cent. upon these 35,530,000 acres to bring their output up to that from the 49,553,000 which would be needed on existing levels of crop yield. It is an entrancing calculation which may be faulted in detail, but which is valid enough in its broad outline. It does, however, ignore the facts that to reach this output agriculture must make greater use of both foreign and home resources in fertilizers, machinery, labour, and finance. The gross output in food may be raised by 40 per cent.; the net output considered as new wealth will be far less. And the economist will

Men can, as the first men did, live by bread alone; but there is then nothing to distinguish them from the beast. Man ceased to be all an animal and nothing more when he spared from his primary preoccupation with his stomach and his genital organs a moment to express with his hands and his mouth a sense of the relationship between the world outside and the mind within him. And ever since, man has been the possessor of what, for want of a better word, must be called a culture: a culture subconsciously absorbed and developed from his environment and unconsciously expressed in his mode of living, which is a true culture. The culture consciously evolved or borrowed to fill a subconsciously felt vacuum is a culture in the modern, commonly accepted sense of the word. The distinction is a fundamental one for the present purpose; for the one flows from an active association between man and his environment, and the other is an artificial titillation of the senses deliberately administered as a stimulant, a sedative or a fashion, unspontaneously and exotically—but not necessarily undesirably, for it is a pleasant and useful device by society to entertain or instruct itself in the ancillary arts of living.

The land, as the perpetual companion of man during most of his history, drew the pattern of his civilization in an unmistakable manner. The tiller and the soil were a partnership in which each shaped the figure of the other: the peasant by the picture which he painted upon the face of the countryside, the soil by the influence which it exercised upon the mental and physical equipment of the men who lived by and upon it. This aspect is one which no attempt at an analysis of the history of a society and its land can ignore; although in the pursuit of what may seem to be the truth in this matter the hunter is a wolf that follows a flying fawn made the more elusive by the fog that envelops the chase, a fourth dimensional fog which has had the curious effect upon all who try to peer through it of making time past appear to

243

be compounded of innocence and infinite charm, beauty and divine benevolence, and giving time present a cloven hoof.

With the definition in mind of culture as a spontaneous, indigenous expression of a particular mode of life, what can be said of the impact of the British countryside upon the men and women who have had to do with it?

In the early stages the association between the two—the people and the land—was intimate and exclusive of almost all else; although in fact there was one other element to come in, the Church. Humanity had drawn from the soil its sustenance—and of that earlier chapters have dealt; its material possessions, for there was no other source of these; and its imaginings, its thoughts upon the supernatural and the natural order of things, which literate man later called religion. As a man's house was hewn out of the forest, his cooking pots made from the clay, his clothes woven from his own flax and the fleeces of his sheep, so his thoughts, when they ranged beyond the prime necessity of keeping himself alive, sprang from the earth with which he was in so close and constant a contact. His religion was home-spun around the luck of the chase, and it survives in the reindeer horns of Abbot's Bromley; around the fertility of his wife and his crops and stock, and the lewd Sheila-na-Gig device joins hands with the festival of a new John Barleycorn at Easter and the Rogationtide ritual in the parish church; around the green man who lived in the dark woods, but who now survives in roof boss and inn sign; and around the supernatural miracles of nature, which remain under the surface of the countryside: for when Cecil Torr asked a Wreyland father why, to cure a ruptured child, he had passed it through a riven ash tree, Torr had the reply that the rupture in the child should mend as the tree healed, and anyway it would do at least as much good as 'sloppin' water over'n in church'. A man's thoughts, habits, possessions and pursuits met in the land, whence they came; or, for the warrior, in the magic sword and Grendel-haunted bog, because his crops were bloody ones, not wheaten.

The Saxon life had a beauty of simplicity when it is seen in retrospect; and each century that passes adds a rosier tint to the spectacles through which the past is viewed. To the men who lived in this past there would probably have seemed little to commend it had they known any better, had they had an urban yardstick against which to measure it. But culturally considered it was a self-contained, self-sufficient life in which the mental and physical attributes of a man flowed entirely from his environment; and his conception of morality was conditioned by his pagan preoccupations and was built around the good-neighbourliness which was necessary if a family was to survive in a cold and hostile world, and around the courage and loyalties which were the mental armour of the fighting man.

The first alien influence which crept into the rustic simplicity of Saxon Britain was the Christian Church. The early missionary fathers brought with them an oriental verbal imagery which must have fallen strangely upon the ears of a Teutonic soldier-farmer; but they also brought a catalogue of virtues which marched fairly closely with those which necessity and tradition had built up in the native culture, because they were the virtues which are common to all decent, kindly folk whether they worship a Chinese sage, a Scandinavian godling, or a Hebrew carpenter. Because Augustine and his master were wise men who permitted the practices of paganism to be incorporated imperceptibly into the Roman calendar, the transition from the old bucolic religion to the new was an easy one; and the combined belief settled down at the very roots of British living. The Church, indeed, became the half of a man, and a principal foundation, with the land, of the life of the medieval peasantry.

The two forces—daily contact with the soil and the Christian concern for the soul—made a nicely balanced cultural diet: the one an ever-present, endless source of much toil and some pleasure in the result, and the other a welcome escape from reality and a promise of a paradise in heaven which most men and women knew they could never find on earth.

There were no extraneous intrusions into the self-contained existence of the countryside; and each man had to make his life from the materials which were to his hand. The blessed mutter of the Mass was a familiar and an incomprehensible incantation intoned above the ancient mixture of work in the village fields, of home-building, weaving, brewing, birth and death, of manor court inquisitions into unscoured ditches and the archidiaconal visitations into the concupiscence of the priest, all spiced by the occasional hue and cry, fornication, and alehouse gossip: a mixture compounded of the vastly familiar ingredients of village life. That life was often filthy, full of misery and starvation, cold and cruel, and the family harp was often tuned to mourning; but it was all of a piece. The joy that was in it was the joy of familiarity; and its homogeneity sprang from the fact that the houses, the customs, the pagan beliefs that had been continued in the Christian dogma all grew out of the soil. The whole bred an overwhelming sense of community which gave the village a profounder significance than can be found in any part of the normal living of the twentieth century.

It was, however, an inarticulate culture; and it has been left to later generations to write its virtues into it; and none can know whether they are true or not. Was each man his own minute philosopher, as Kingsley said? 'The oftener one sees the better one knows; and the better one knows the more one loves.' Did medieval man think, with Jefferies, 'I do not want change. I want the old and loved things'?

Did he in fact make a blessing out of Adam's curse, and find the greatest of his pride in seeing his ewes graze and his lambs suck? Or was he like the tractor-driver in the *Economist* who, asked what he thought of as he ploughed, replied, 'I looks at the bloody earth and I says "Blast it"'? The reaction of the intelligent, ambitious countryman through the centuries has usually been to get out of the countryside as fast as he can. 'Country children go to plough! They become clerks or some skimmy-dish thing or other.'

Whether good or bad—or, if the reader asks what is good and evil—whether a completely satisfying thing or not, the venerable bucolic pattern of culture continued, modified but basically intact, until the gates of mercy were all shut up and the intimacy between man and the land was sharply ended by the centuries of enclosure, of the rise of industry and the decline of the peasantry, and of the departure of rural self-sufficiency. The decay of the old ways cannot be pin-pointed in time. It set in at different places in different centuries and in different ways. Early Tudor sheep-ranching swept away whole villages; but 400 years later the culture of the lost hamlets of Midland England still survived only a little damaged in the cultural backwaters of the Hebrides where 'as late as the middle of the nineteenth century it was more like that of the pre-Roman Iron Age in southern England'; where the black houses with both cattle and family sheltering beneath the one roof and a fire that has not been out for a century are still found; and where pots boiled by heated stones dropped into them, rude home-made pottery, and archaic quern mills are still living memories. The remoter Welsh hills could also, at the beginning of the present century, still boast the survival of an active folk lore which was incredibly ancient and the long houses of which the pattern had descended little changed over 2,000 years.

When the perfect, earthy, primitive, and unassuming

is their prayer; and it may also be given to them to maintain the fabric of the world. And, strangely enough, it is the man from the town who, reversing the ancient course, is often coming into the country to bring new life into the old industry which his ancestors abandoned.